Also by Ana Sampson

She is Fierce:
Brave, bold and beautiful poems by women

Ana Sampson

SHE WILL SOAR

Bright, brave poems about
escape and freedom by women

MACMILLAN

Published 2020 by Macmillan Children's Books
an imprint of Pan Macmillan
The Smithson, 6 Briset Street, London EC1M 5NR
Associated companies throughout the world
www.panmacmillan.com

ISBN 978-1-5290-4004-3

1 3 5 7 9 8 6 4 2

A CIP catalogue record for this book is available from the British Library.

Printed and bound by CPI Group (UK) Ltd, Croydon CR0 4YY

For my parents, with love and thanks

Contents

'A land where I could be a queen' – Growing Up

'What if this road . . .' – Travels over Land

'Golden windows in a wall' – Words Can Set You Free

'My wild hair backward blown' – Taking Flight

'It's better with all the banners flying' – Courage, Hope and Resilience

'Chasing weightlessness' – The Final Frontier

'It's the sea I want' – Voyages by Verse

'Dream me mermaid' – Flights of Fancy

'Silence and a space of sleep' – Travels towards Tranquillity

Introduction

I'd like to travel back through time and tell my schoolgirl self that, one day, I'd consider poetry to be a magic carpet. (Although, I suspect she would have looked up from wrestling with a knotty slice of D. H. Lawrence only to roll her eyes!) To me now, though, there is no more efficient escape hatch from the daily grind than a poem. In just a handful of lines, a poet can snatch us up to dangle us over mountain ranges, sweep us into starry space or plunge us into the ocean's green depths. Poetry can take you anywhere.

When I began gathering work by women poets and reading about their lives, I started to understand just how much was stacked against them. To make any kind of art, an artist requires leisure, learning and liberty — all privileges that have been harder for women than men to access throughout history and into our own time. During most periods, only a handful of aristocratic women enjoyed the time, education and opportunity to aspire to a literary career and, even then, they were often mocked or condemned for their daring. 'Intense thought spoils a lady's features,' asserted eighteenth-century critic William Rose, and gentlemen of the press raged against women who neglected their domestic duties to write. Well into the twentieth and twenty-first centuries, women's writing has routinely been dismissed and undervalued.

Female writers have, therefore, always had good cause to write about the liberties they have so often been denied. What began as a book about travel – through this world and others, through the air and over the waves, into space and beneath the earth – transformed in the gathering into a collection of bright, brave poems about escape and freedom. From frustrated housewives to passionate activists, here is a bold choir of voices shouting for independence and celebrating their power.

This collection was conceived in 2019. These words — about

wanderlust and longing to be free – took on a deeper resonance as the world locked down in the face of a global pandemic. The verses I had collected were suddenly my only means of travel or escape and felt all the more necessary for it. We don't know how long our wings will be clipped in some ways but, like many others, I have found comfort and a taste of liberty every time I have opened a book. I hope this volume can add to that reservoir of consolation.

There are many reasons to be cheerful about the status of women's writing. Women fill stadiums, win prizes and scale the bestseller lists. Digital ecosystems such as Instagram have created a new generation of poetry lovers and enabled talented poets to leapfrog the genre's traditional gatekeepers to reach readers. Publishers and critics have acknowledged the imbalances of the past and are newly mindful of their responsibility to produce a more diverse canon for the future. Some of the women in these pages remained unpublished or unpraised during their lifetimes, and I find it completely wonderful to know that they are moving new readers now.

I apologize, as always, for omissions – it was painful to have to whittle down a many-splendoured longlist to something that wouldn't fill a whole shelf – but I wish you as much pleasure reading these poems as I had foraging for them. One of the greatest beauties of poetry is that it reminds us that we are not, and never have been, alone. These women walked this way before us, and they have left us these bright threads to follow through the dark. For the days when the world weighs heavy on us, for the days when the struggle seems fiercest, I hope you will find a parachute in these pages.

Ana Sampson, 2020

'I smelt the smell of distance and longed for another existence' – Wanderlust and Dreams of Freedom

Here are poems that give us permission to dream, whether we are indulging in fantasies of a new life during a golden café afternoon, or whiling away a long lesson on a summer's day. These poets beautifully express the desire to break free – to be, as Safia Elhillo writes, 'ungovernable'.

Elinor Wylie imagines herself a tiny, twinkling thing, fleeing the world through an escape hatch so tiny and enchanted that she cannot be pursued. We hear from one of the world's most celebrated recluses, Emily Dickinson, who locked herself down in the family home for two decades. She spoke to visitors through a door and treated the local children by lowering baskets of sweets from her window, but in her poetry she yearned for flight and freedom. Kate Wakeling, Carol Ann Duffy and civil rights activist Georgia Douglas Johnson urge us to throw open the door. The world is wide and waiting.

The Distance

Over the sounding sea,
Off the wandering sea
I smelt the smell of distance
And longed for another existence.
Smell of pineapple, maize, and myrrh,
Parrot-feather and monkey-fur,
Brown spice,
Blue ice,
Fields of tobacco and tea and rice,
And soundless snows,
And snowy cotton,
Otto of rose
Incense in an ivory palace,
Jungle rivers rich and rotten,
Slumbering valleys,
Smouldering mountains,
Rank morasses
And frozen fountains,
Black molasses and purple wine,
Coral and pearl and tar and brine,
The smell of panther and polar-bear
And leopard-lair
And mermaid-hair
Came from the four-cornered distance,
And I longed for another existence.

Eleanor Farjeon

Maybe I'll Be The First

In the car, shreds of 8am light pool in,
the half-moons under her eyes.
She told me she's been searching all her life –
her spine now a heavy root from years of reaching
and stretching and slipping between rock and struggle.
She is a small tree, in a big storm
refusing to be displaced.
Yet every so often
anger strips her tongue
into a lashing whip,
burns hot coals in the pit
of her stomach, blows back smoke
through her heart.
In her village, she watched many close to her fall. She told me
there were murmurs of dreamers hearing an oasis calling,
whispering honey as they slept and schemed,
letting the sweetness drip in deep waves. She said
she wants to know just once, if it is as warm as the dreamers
    say.

For my mother, I am trying to learn what freedom looks like
in this body of mine. What it tastes like in this mouth or feels
  like running
through the thick of my hair and the small of my hands. I am
  trying
to grasp freedom with my teeth, the tips of my toes. Trying to
  catch it
on my eyelash, for her.
She does not know freedom,
has never known freedom,
but I've seen it
looking good, sauntering elsewhere.
I want it.
The choice to go
where I choose when I am ready.

Michelle Tiwo

'I smelt the smell of distance and longed for another existence' — Wanderlust

border/softer

in the new year or when i grow up or
if i live through the night i want to be

ungovernable   no longer a citizen
to any of the names assigned my body

& then how boundless could i make my life
which for all its smallness still exhausts me

balancing act of all my margins all my conjugations
of cannot   if i live through the night i will bleed

into all my edges until i am no longer a stroke
of some careless man's pen   after

a particularly liquid lunch churchill was said
to have created [   ] with a stroke of his [   ]

& isn't a map only a joke we all agreed into a fact
& where can I touch the equator & how will i know

i am touching it   & where is the end of my country
the beginning of the next how will i know i've crossed over

Safia Elhillo

untitled poem – on travel

It is a pleasant thing to roam abroad,
And gaze on scenes and objects strange and grand;
To sail in mighty ships o'er distant seas,
And roam the mountains of a foreign land.

Effie Afton

Galway Dreaming

I watch the gush of life in the May sunshine.
Galway is slow and golden syrup.
I sit outside the same café all afternoon
slowly sipping beers
watching students cavort
like the swallows above the town,
spring sun shines on my face,
I could not be more happy.
My heart leaps like the fish
in the shimmering river
and I let my gladness run free.
I imagine living here in Ireland,
how I would write another book,
a tender and poetic story and
I'd marry a strapping lad
with soft green-blue eyes,
sometimes we'd drink whiskey
and watch the full moon rise,
my cheeks would be pink
and my body a little plump
but my husband would cherish me,
he'd be faithful and steady and strong,
he'd pick me up and make me laugh like a girl.
I'd have a slower heartbeat.
I'd write poems on the beach each morning
and swim a mile in the bay at sunset.
It would be a good and happy life.

London would become a blurred fog,
a memory of bright lights, big talk and speed
and I dream this dream all day,
I dream this dream,
with one slow
exhalation.

Salena Godden

Escape

When foxes eat the last gold grape,
And the last white antelope is killed,
I shall stop fighting and escape
Into a little house I'll build.

But first I'll shrink to fairy size,
With a whisper no one understands,
Making blind moons of all your eyes,
And muddy roads of all your hands.

And you may grope for me in vain
In hollows under the mangrove root,
Or where, in apple-scented rain,
The silver wasp-nests hang like fruit.

Elinor Wylie

Your World

Your world is as big as you make it.
I know, for I used to abide
In the narrowest nest in a corner,
My wings pressing close to my side.

But I sighted the distant horizon
Where the skyline encircled the sea
And I throbbed with a burning desire
To travel this immensity.

I battered the cordons around me
And cradled my wings on the breeze,
Then soared to the uttermost reaches
With rapture, with power, with ease!

Georgia Douglas Johnson

Not knowing when the Dawn will come

Not knowing when the Dawn will come,
I open every Door,
Or has it Feathers, like a Bird,
Or Billows, like a Shore?

Emily Dickinson

The Instructions

1. How to spot THE INSTRUCTIONS

THE INSTRUCTIONS come in all shapes and sizes.
They are often found in and around:
- *Tall buildings with statues of lions outside*
- *Faces with an angry expression*
- *Faces with a smile seen only in the mouth but (crucially) not in the eyes*

2. The other instructions

There are plenty of *other* sorts of instructions, which can of course be useful.
For example:
- *Try not to insert any part of your body into this pond: it contains an irritated crocodile*
- *For best results, keep both eyes open while landing this lopsided helicopter*
- *Do not under any circumstances eat the angry man's sandwich*

3. What THE INSTRUCTIONS want

You see, THE INSTRUCTIONS aren't here to help you.
They want to help someone or something else.
THE INSTRUCTIONS say things like:
- *No one's ever done THAT before: it CAN'T be a good idea*

'I smelt the smell of distance and longed for another existence' – Wanderlust

- *Please do the SAME thing as all those OTHER people over THERE*
- *Hear that person talking in the PARTICULARLY loud voice? They must DEFINITELY be RIGHT.*

4. If you follow THE INSTRUCTIONS

If you follow THE INSTRUCTIONS it is unlikely anyone will ever be very cross with you. If you follow THE INSTRUCTIONS you are guaranteed to feel neat and tidy (but also a little short of breath)

5. If you don't follow THE INSTRUCTIONS

You will likely face some tricky moments. Apologies for this. However, there is also a good chance that something

Strangeexcitingremarkableunexpectedslightly-frighteningbutbrightlycoloured

will happen.

6. The choice

is yours.

Kate Wakeling

Away and See

Away and see an ocean suck at a boiled sun
and say to someone things I'd blush even to dream.
Slip off your dress in a high room over the harbour.
Write to me soon.

New fruits sing on the flipside of night in a market
of language, light, a tune from the chapel nearby
stopping you dead, the peach in your palm respiring.
Taste it for me.

Away and see the things that words give a name to, the flight
of syllables, wingspan stretching a noun. Test words
wherever they live; listen and touch, smell, believe.
Spell them with love.

Skedaddle. Somebody chaps at the door at a year's end,
    hopeful.
Away and see who it is. Let in the new, the vivid,
horror and pity, passion, the stranger holding the future.
Ask him his name.

Nothing's the same as anything else. Away and see
for yourself. Walk. Fly. Take a boat till land reappears,
altered for ever, ringing its bells, alive. Go on. G'on. Gon.
Away and see.

Carol Ann Duffy

'A girl unbridled' – Feeling Free

These are poems to shout and shimmy to, united by the sheer sense of exhilaration with which they leap off the page. Here are all kinds of ways to get free, from Sarah Crossan stomping splashily through streams and Olive Runner racing the wind, to Amy Lowell laughing in the bath. (Also, please do seek out the Shirelles singing 'What Does a Girl Do?' before you read Marilyn Hacker's bold and jaunty answer in 'Mythology' – it's terrific.) There is a certain flavour of freedom I hadn't felt for years that comes back to me vividly in Esther Morgan's 'The Long Holidays'.

These are writers who have found their voices and are not afraid of raising them, celebrating women who – as Carole Satyamurti gleefully notes – 'sang their own numbers'.

Freedom

Give me the long, straight road before me,
    A clear, cold day with a nipping air,
Tall, bare trees to run on beside me,
    A heart that is light and free from care.
Then let me go! – I care not whither
    My feet may lead, for my spirit shall be
Free as the brook that flows to the river,
    Free as the river that flows to the sea.

Olive Runner

Mythology

Penelope as a garçon manqué
weaves sonnets on a barstool among sailors,
tapping her iambs out on the brass rail. Ours
is not the high-school text. Persephone
a.k.a Télémaque-who-tagged-along,
sleeps off her lunch on an Italian train
headed for Paris, while Ulysse-Maman
plugs into the Shirelles singing her song
('What Does a Girl Do?'). What does a girl do
but walk across the world, her kid in tow,
stopping at stations on the way, with friends
to tie her to the mast when she gets too
close to the edge? And when the voyage ends,
what does a girl do? Girl, that's up to you.

Marilyn Hacker

Freedom Poem

Breathe
In.
Breathe
Out.
Gasp,
Sigh,
Scream,
Shout.
Spread your arms wide and smile
find yourself
find your style.
Make yourself tall, as tall can be
do the impossible
one time,
two times,
three
and say out loud
'I am Free'.

Michaela Morgan

The Long Holidays

The day stretches ahead – nothing but
grass and sky grass and sky grass and sky grass and sky
as far as the eye can see

nothing but
sky and grass sky and grass sky and grass sky and grass

and the wind galloping hard over the fields
like a riderless horse.

Esther Morgan

In Wellies

Oh to be in Magherabeg
Where I was adult free
From sun up til head down,
Stomping through streams in worn out wellies,
Chasing rams down to the Swilly.
They called me in only to eat
Rock buns for tea
And say the rosary –
 Oh clement , oh loving, oh sweet Virgin Mary.
I never knew then what stranger danger was –
Warned only to 'mind that road'
Which had killed two of my grandmother's dogs.
At the close of summer
I hid beneath beds
So I wouldn't have to leave
Knowing it wasn't the hills I would miss
But being a girl unbridled.

Sarah Crossan

Lines Composed in a Wood on a Windy Day

My soul is awakened, my spirit is soaring
   And carried aloft on the wings of the breeze;
For above and around me the wild wind is roaring,
   Arousing to rapture the earth and the seas.

The long withered grass in the sunshine is glancing,
   The bare trees are tossing their branches on high;
The dead leaves beneath them are merrily dancing,
   The white clouds are scudding across the blue sky.

I wish I could see how the ocean is lashing
   The foam of its billows to whirlwinds of spray;
I wish I could see how its proud waves are dashing,
   And hear the wild roar of their thunder today!

Anne Brontë

Londoner

Scarcely two hours back in the country
and I'm shopping in East Finchley High Road
in a cotton skirt, a cardigan, jandals —
or flipflops as people call them here,
where February's winter. Aren't I cold?
The neighbours in their overcoats are smiling
at my smiles and not at my bare toes:
they know me here.
                        I hardly know myself,
yet. It takes me until Monday evening,
walking from the office after dark
to Westminster Bridge. It's cold, it's foggy,
the traffic's as abominable as ever,
and there across the Thames is County Hall,
that uninspired stone body, floodlit.
It makes me laugh. In fact, it makes me sing.

Fleur Adcock

She Showed Me Her Dreams

On a winter day when frost crackled
static in the wireless, the window lost
light and dark slid through the glass
into my eyes, she poked the fire to
make the flames dance on the coals.

'Look,' she said, 'tell me what you see.'

I watched serpents glide from caverns,
their mouths wide. I saw forests fall
to ashes and children burning.
The devil glowered from the embers.
My face and knees prickled heat and
gravestone shivers chilled my spine.

She stood behind me against the cold.
'Look again,' she said.
'Can you see where the yellow is
growing golden? Can you see the
sun rising on the mountains?'

I looked and I saw, and I saw the
women striding into the dawn,
their gowns flickering red and green,
hurrying to meet the morning.

Norah Hanson

Let Me Count the Ways

These are the ways you make me feel:
one ice cube clinking in a wine glass on a hot day
overfilling my mouth with my mum's food
    when I haven't been home in a while
every hair on my head lifting in anticipation
my first sip of coffee
confident muscles stretching before a perfect dive bomb into
    a cool, blue pool in front of the lifeguards and a sign that
      says:
    no dive bombing
family, but the one you choose
a high note on a violin
the absolute joy at meeting a freshly-wrought human being
    by someone you love
the split second of the heart leap when you're swinging
    on a swing at the upswing before gravity claims you
bliss at dancing your hardest to good techno and you look
  around
    and everyone is beautiful
the cranium split when you think a completely new thought
    and the world rushes in
thick snow over everything familiar
the searing burn from sitting too close to a fire.

Sheena Patel

Bath

The day is fresh-washed and fair, and there is a smell of tulips and narcissus in the air.

The sunshine pours in at the bath-room window and bores through the water in the bath-tub in lathes and planes of greenish-white. It cleaves the water into flaws like a jewel, and cracks it to bright light.

Little spots of sunshine lie on the surface of the water and dance, dance, and their reflections wobble deliciously over the ceiling; a stir of my finger sets them whirring, reeling. I move a foot and the planes of light in the water jar. I lie back and laugh, and let the green-white water, the sun-flawed beryl water, flow over me. The day is almost too bright to bear, the green water covers me from the too bright day. I will lie here awhile and play with the water and the sun spots. The sky is blue and high. A crow flaps by the window, and there is a whiff of tulips and narcissus in the air.

Amy Lowell

Ourstory

Let us now praise women
with feet glass slippers wouldn't fit;

not the patient, nor even the embittered
ones who kept their place,

but awkward women, tenacious with truth,
whose elbows disposed of the impossible;

who split seams, who wouldn't wait,
take no, take sedatives;

who sang their own numbers, went uninsured,
knew best what they were missing.

Our misfit foremothers are joining forces
underground, their dusts mingling

breast-bone with scapula, forehead
with forehead. Their steady mass

bursts locks; lends a springing foot
to our vaulting into enormous rooms.

Carole Satyamurti

Megan Married Herself

She arrived at the country mansion in a silver limousine.
She'd sent out invitations and everything:
her name written twice with '&' in the middle,
the calligraphy of coupling.
She strode down the aisle to 'At Last' by Etta James,
faced the celebrant like a keen soldier reporting for duty,
her voice shaky yet sure. I do. I do.
'You may now kiss the mirror.' Applause. Confetti.
Every single one of the hundred and forty guests
deemed the service 'unimprovable'.
Especially the vows. So 'from the heart'.
Her wedding gown was ivory; pointedly off-white,
'After all, we've shared a bed for thirty-two years,'
she quipped in her first speech,
'I'm hardly virginal if you know what I mean.'
(No one knew *exactly* what she meant.)
Not a soul questioned their devotion.
You only had to look at them. Hand cupped in hand.
Smiling out of the same eyes. You could sense
their secret language, bone-deep, blended blood.
Toasts were frequent, tearful. One guest
eyed his wife – hovering harmlessly at the bar – and
imagined what his life might've been if
he'd responded, years ago, to that offer in his head:
I'm the only one who will ever truly understand you.
Marry me, Derek. I love you. Marry me.'
At the time, he hadn't taken his proposal seriously.

He recharged his champagne flute, watched
the newlywed cut her five-tiered cake, both hands
on the knife. 'Is it too late for us to try?' Derek whispered
to no one, as the bride glided herself onto the dance floor,
taking turns first to lead then follow.

Caroline Bird

'A land where I could be a queen' – Growing Up

Growing up is hard to do, as the world's myths and legends have always told us. In Eavan Boland's quietly anguished 'The Pomegranate' the poet compares herself to bereft Ceres, whose daughter was spirited to the underworld for half the year. This mother acknowledges the limits of her power and the bittersweet necessity of letting go. In an intriguing reimagining of the same myth by Nikita Gill, a defiant Persephone embraces her abduction, feeling herself freer on her dark throne than in her mother's shadow.

These poems introduce us to parents both tender and terrible, and children striving to step out solo. What is childhood but the study of escape and the hope that, once alone, we will find – as Shazea Quraishi writes – that we 'walked taller, balanced better'? Wide futures and bright lights are calling as these poets fly the nest for freedom.

The Mother

The mother is a weapon you load
yourself into, little bullet.

The mother is glass through which
you see, in excruciating detail, yourself.

The mother is landscape.
See how she thinks of a tree
and fills a forest with the repeated thought.

Before the invention of cursive
the mother is manuscript.

The mother is sky.
See how she wears a shawl of starlings,
how she pulls the thrumming around her shoulders.

The mother is a prism.
The mother is a gun.

See how light passes through her.
See how she fires.

Maggie Smith

Hedgehog

Its leg was not broken. It was not homeless.
It clenched in my hands, a living flinch.
You cannot love so much and live,
it whispered, its spines clicking like teeth.
I hid it from itself in a cardboard box.

Overnight it nibbled a hole and slipped away.
I cried so much my mother thought I'd never stop.
She said, *you cannot love so* – and yet
I grew to average size and amused a lot of people
with my prickliness and brilliant escapes.

Polly Clark

The Pomegranate

The only legend I have ever loved is
the story of a daughter lost in hell.
And found and rescued there.
Love and blackmail are the gist of it.
Ceres and Persephone the names.
And the best thing about the legend is
I can enter it anywhere. And have.
As a child in exile in
a city of fogs and strange consonants,
I read it first and at first I was
an exiled child in the crackling dusk of
the underworld, the stars blighted. Later
I walked out in a summer twilight
searching for my daughter at bed-time.
When she came running I was ready
to make any bargain to keep her.
I carried her back past whitebeams
and wasps and honey-scented buddleias.
But I was Ceres then and I knew
winter was in store for every leaf
on every tree on that road.
Was inescapable for each one we passed.
And for me.
                    It is winter
and the stars are hidden.
I climb the stairs and stand where I can see
my child asleep beside her teen magazines,

her can of Coke, her plate of uncut fruit.
The pomegranate! How did I forget it?
She could have come home and been safe
and ended the story and all
our heart-broken searching but she reached
out a hand and plucked a pomegranate.
She put out her hand and pulled down
the French sound for apple and
the noise of stone and the proof
that even in the place of death,
at the heart of legend, in the midst
of rocks full of unshed tears
ready to be diamonds by the time
the story was told, a child can be
hungry. I could warn her. There is still a chance.
The rain is cold. The road is flint-coloured.
The suburb has cars and cable television.
The veiled stars are above ground.
It is another world. But what else
can a mother give her daughter but such
beautiful rifts in time?
If I defer the grief I will diminish the gift.
The legend will be hers as well as mine.
She will enter it. As I have.
She will wake up. She will hold
the papery flushed skin in her hand.
And to her lips. I will say nothing.

Eavan Boland

Persephone to Demeter

Do you remember what happened
the first time I touched a pomegranate shrub?
Instead of bursting to a full red fruit,
it wilted and mottled under my fingers
until you snatched it and brought it back to life.

We both knew in that moment,
I nurtured something in my chest you
couldn't bring yourself to love.
So you kept me hidden, deep in a forest
where no one could find me,

the darkness an ugliness festering
under this, my pretty nymph skin.
But, Mama, he found me. He saw me
nourish this beast in the woods,
fell in love with the part of me that
no one else could, promised me a land where

I could be a queen and not another version of you,
a place where I could unleash my flaws and fury
without having to disappoint you. They told you
they could bring me back to you, to pacify your anger,
so you could bring back the spring.

Nikita Gill

38

The Window
after Marie Howe

Once in a lifetime, you will gesture
at an open window, tell the one who
detests the queerness in you that dead
daughters do not disappoint, free your
sore knees from inching towards a kind
of reprieve, declare yourself genderless
as hawk or sparrow: an encumbered body
let loose from its cage. You will refuse
your mother's rage, her spit, her tongue
heavy like the heaviest of stones. Her
anger is like the sun, which is like love,
which is the easiest thing, even on the
hardest of days. You will linger, knowing
that this standing before an open window
is what the living do: that they sometimes
reconsider at the slightest touch of grace.

Mary Jean Chan

Obedience, or The Lying Tale

I will do everything you tell me, Mother.
I will charm three gold hairs
From the demon's head.
I will choke the mouse that gnaws
an apple tree's roots and keep its skin
for a glove. To the wolf, I will be
pretty and kind and curtsy
his crossing of my path.

The forest, vocal
even in its somber tread, rages.
A slope ends in a pit of foxes
drunk on rotten brambles of berries
and the raccoons ransack
a rabbit's unmasked hole.
What do they find but a winter's heap
of droppings? A stolen nest, the cracked shell

of another creature's child.
I imagine this is the rabbit way
and I will not stray, Mother,
into the forest's thick,
where the trees meet the dark,
though I have known misgivings
of light as hot hand that flickers
against my neck. The path ends

at a river I must cross. I will wait
for the ferryman
to motion me through. Into the waves
he etches with his oar
a new story: a silent girl runs away,
a silent girl is never safe.
I will take his oar in my hand. I will learn
the boat's rocking and bring myself back

and forth. To be good
Is the hurricane of caution.
I will know indecision's rowing,
the water I lap into my lap
as he shakes his withered head.
Behind me is the forest. Before me
the field, a loose run of grass. I stay
in the river, Mother, I study escape.

Jennifer Chang

kids

Our bones stuck like honey
Silken gestures grazing ground
As we flew over handlebars
And relished in dotting our bloodied scars with the same tiny
    digits that made shapes with carbon-backed stars.
The nonsense made sense in its cherry-rich taste of speaking
    a language of pulling funny faces.
The fear of inferior was nothing but a shifting canvas that
    smelt like summer
Shedding our winter skin to become a
Firecracker of innocence
An uncorrupted, feverishly disruptive
Blazing ball of wonder
And when we expanded from its amber shell
Spitting sparks as we embraced the swell
Each filament of learning spun a grand farewell
And spoke a greeting to the less bright
Other side of where those taller weren't glowing
I'm sure we'd never have grown up if
We'd been told where we were going.

Charly Cox

The worlds

My mum made us many worlds
overlapping in bright circles,
and made us the shape-shifting shoes
to stride into them.

She made England
and she made Australians,
mouths filed with eucalyptus phrases;

She made shop-owners,
plying our biscuits and lemonade
to ramblers in our lane

and she made ramblers,
free from the hard charm of destination.

She made an artist's daughters,
story-hearers and selective believers.
She made tree-dwellers,
trend-leavers and fancy-dress-wearers,

irregular pegs. She made the round holes
shimmy, she made silly,
she made kindness, she made calm.

My mum makes us the world
as wide as the world
and as small as the circle of her arms.

Rachel Piercey

Praise Song for My Mother

You were
water to me
deep and bold and fathoming

You were
moon's eye to me
pull and grained and mantling

You were
sunrise to me
rise and warm and streaming

You were
the fishes red gill to me
the flame tree's spread to me
the crab's leg/the fried plantain smell
                    replenishing replenishing
Go to your wide futures, you said

Grace Nichols

You May Have Heard of Me

My father was a bear.
He carried me through forest, sky
and over frozen sea. At night
I lay along his back
wrapped in fur and heat
and while I slept, he ran,
never stopping to rest, never
letting me fall.
He showed me how to be as careful as stone,
sharp as thorn and quick
as weather. When he hunted alone
he'd leave me somewhere safe – high up a tree
or deep within a cave.
And then a day went on . . .
He didn't come.
I looked and looked for him.
The seasons changed and changed again.
Sleep became my friend. It even brought my father back.
The dark was like his fur,
the sea's breathing echoed his breathing.
I left home behind, an empty skin.
Alone, I walked taller, balanced better.

So I came to the gates of this city
– tall, black gates with teeth.
Here you find me, keeping my mouth small,
hiding pointed teeth and telling stories,
concealing their truth as I conceal
the thick black fur on my back.

Shazea Quraishi

'What if this road . . .' – Travels over Land

Sheenagh Pugh asks us, 'Who wants to know where a road will go?' In these poems, Helen Burke is striding excitedly out of town. Sasha Dugdale longs to burst from the warm house and walk out into Christmas night. Gillian Allnut and Hollie McNish bike to freedom. Here are journeys by train and carriage, an escape across the sands and plenty of instructions for the intrepid. It's time to shoulder your bag – though be sure to travel light – and begin the journey.

Not all these roads lead somewhere. Not all these roads are real roads. The important thing – always – is to keep on moving.

What if this road

What if this road, that has held no surprises
these many years, decided not to go
home after all; what if it could turn
left or right with no more ado
than a kite-tail? What if its tarry skin
were like a long, supple bolt of cloth,
that is shaken and rolled out, and takes
a new shape from the contours beneath?
And if it chose to lay itself down
in a new way; around a blind corner,
across hills you must climb without knowing
what's on the other side; who would not hanker
to be going, at all risks? Who wants to know
a story's end, or where a road will go?

Sheenagh Pugh

On the Road Through Chang-te

On the last year's trip I enjoyed this place.
I am glad to come back here today.
The fish market is deep in blue shadows.
I can see the smoke for tea rising
From the thatched inn.
The sands of the river beaches
Merge with the white moon.
Along the shore the willows
Wait for their Spring green.
Lines of a poem run through my mind.
I order the carriage to stop for a while.

Sun Yün-feng

Translated by Kenneth Rexroth
and Ling Chung

Divorce

A voice from the dark is calling me.
In the close house I nurse a fire.
Out in the dark cold winds rush free
To the rock heights of my desire.
I smother in the house in the valley below,
Let me out to the night, let me go, let me go.

Spirits that ride the sweeping blast,
Frozen in rigid tenderness,
Wait! for I leave the fire at last
My little-love's warm loneliness.
I smother in the house in the valley below,
Let me out to the night, let me go, let me go.

High on the hills are beating drums.
Clear from a line of marching men
To the rock's edge the hero comes.
He calls me and he calls again.
On the hill there is fighting, victory, or quick death,
In the house is the fire, which I fan with sick breath.
I smother in the house in the valley below,
Let me out to the dark, let me go, let me go!

Anna Wickham

The dusk settles at about two
One side of the sky hankers after the day
and its vapour trails. The other is dragged down
like fabric in a dogs's mouth
and its's a relief, we can stop pretending
and close the curtains and light the gasfire.
The hills and moors recede like silent planets
and the rain hisses on the sea, and the dining chairs
are moved into the living room. Outside it feels like nothing:
like black space. The carpet is littered with tissue crowns
and ribbons and the ash of fallen laughter

Come out with me. Come now, just pull the door to,
And along the pavements, doesn't matter where
Just outside, keep walking, and if there's a hill climb it

Sasha Dugdale

The Footprint

Of the fleeing man I have
only the footprint,
the weight of his body,
and the wind that blows him.
No signs, no name,
no country or town,
only the damp
shell of his footprint,
only this syllable
absorbed by the sand
and the earth, Veronica
who murmured it to me.

Only the anguish
that hurries his flight:
hammering pulse,
gasping breath,
glistening sweat,
teeth on edge,
and the hard dry wind
that hits his back.

And the thorn he leaps,
the marsh he crosses,
the bush that hides him
and the sun that reveals him,
the hill that helps him,
and the one that betrays him,
the root that trips him
and God who gets him to his feet.

And his daughter, the blood
the calls out through him:
the footprint, Lord,
the bright footprint,
the mouthless cry,
the footprint, the footprint!

Holy sands
eat up his sign.
Dogs of mist,
cover his track.
Falling night,
swallow in one gulp
the great, sweet
mark of a man.

I see, I count
the two thousand footprints.
I go running, running
across old Earth,
mixing up his
poor tracks with mine,
or I stop and erase them
with my wild hair,
or facedown I lick
away the footprints.

But the white Earth
turns eternal,
stretches endless
as a chain,
lengthens out into a snake,
and the Lord God does not break its back.
And the footprints go on
to the end of the world.

Gabriela Mistral

Translated by Ursula K. Le Guin

Autobiography in Five Chapters

I

I walk down the street.
There is a deep hole in the sidewalk
I fall in.
I am lost . . .
I am hopeless.
It isn't my fault
It takes forever to find a way out.

II

I walk down the same street.
There is a deep hole in the sidewalk.
I pretend I don't see it.
I fall in again.
I can't believe I'm in the same place.
But it isn't my fault.
It still takes a long time to get out.

III

I walk down the same street.
There is a deep hole in the sidewalk.
I see it is there.
I still fall in . . . it's a habit
My eyes are open; I know where I am;
It is my fault.
I get out immediately.

IV

I walk down the same street.
There is a deep hole in the sidewalk.
I walk around it.

V

I walk down another street.

Portia Nelson

The Road Out of Town

When will I take you, I ask –
the road out?
Will it be tomorrow? Will it?

Oh, let it be tomorrow –
sweet as a peach that road
and you, juicy with laughter.
Rich that road, as rich as rich
with peacock beginnings
and myself with the shackles and the blindfold gone
and this other road – forgotten.
At first we will be dizzy with the joy of it
but that won't matter – no –
just the feel of the road under our feet
shaking the dust of ages,
the cruel hands of time from ourselves.
Just the being gone will be enough.

No barriers. No signposts.
Just the sun shining on new black tar.
The smell of it under our feet.
And my little famine bones, mending again.
With each bold step as further out of town
I with my singing heart and my whistling soul am led.

And you will look around – oh yes
and only know that I am gone.
You will see the space I have left and say:
'Why yes – there was somewhere else she had to be,
a path she always had to tread.'

And you will hear me singing still
as all sing when first they take that single step
on the Road out of Town.

Helen Burke

Cocoon

raincoat zipped to my chin
for the bike ride
to work

hair bunned at the back
to fit in the hood
helmet clipped – tight
        i am waterproof

now pace reaches peak
the pedals attacked
winter tries hard
but the sweat coats my back
until two minutes left
i let myself go
cycling slowed
to unzip my coat
jacket front free
helmet clipped from beneath
hood stripped from my forehead
hairband released
hair ruffled with hands
to cool in the wind
body to elements
airing my skin

at that moment
i open
and peel myself free

i feel as close
to a new butterfly
as i'll ever be

Hollie McNish

Wolves

We are staring at the moon
and I think for a second we become
wolves again.
Screaming at the stars,
growling at the idea
that this night might end
and we will forget this moment,
as in turn we will be forgotten.
Our wild souls captured.

We become wolves,
and for once we are running
for something.
Instead of running from it.

Ruth Awolola

Ode

To depict a (bicycle), you must first come to love (it).
Alexander Blok

I swear by every rule in the bicycle
owner's manual

that I love you, I, who have repeatedly,
painstakingly,

with accompanying declaration of despair,
tried to repair

you, to patch things up,
to maintain a workable relationship.

I have spent sleepless nights
in pondering your parts – those private

and those that all who walk the street
may look at –

wondering what makes you tick
over smoothly, or squeak.

O my trusty steed,
my rusty three-speed,

I would feed you the best oats
if oats

were applicable.
Only linseed oil

will do
to nourish you.

I want
so much to paint

you,
midnight blue

mudgutter black
and standing as you do, ironic

at the rail
provided by the Council –

beautiful
the sun caught in your back wheel –

or at home in the hall, remarkable
among other bicycles,

your handlebars erect.
Allow me to depict

you thus. And though I can't do justice
to your true opinion of the surface

of the road —
put into words

the nice distinctions that you make
among the different sorts of tarmac —

still I'd like to set the record of our travels straight.
I'd have you know that

not with three-in-one
but with my own

heart's
spittle I anoint your moving parts.

Gillian Allnutt

A Winter Ride

Who shall declare the joy of the running!
   Who shall tell of the pleasures of flight!
Springing and spurning the tufts of wild heather,
   Sweeping, wide-winged, through the blue dome of light.
Everything mortal has moments immortal,
   Swift and God-gifted, immeasurably bright.

So with the stretch of the white road before me,
   Shining snowcrystals rainbowed by the sun,
Fields that are white, stained with long, cool, blue shadows,
   Strong with the strength of my horse as we run.
Joy in the touch of the wind and the sunlight!
   Joy! With the vigorous earth I am one.

Amy Lowell

Driving Back Over the Blue Ridge,

you say that the leaves are late in turning.
Half way up the wooded hill to our right
the sun has decanted itself
into a single maple tree.

There are days like that
which sing orange and red
in the forest of our ordinary green.

These are the days we hang our souls upon
as high above them the sun withdraws.

Moya Cannon

'Golden windows in a wall' – Words Can Set You Free

A book is a thing of power. On the shelves of any library are stacked time machines, stately galleons, space shuttles and trapdoors ready to plunge the reader into unfamiliar landscapes, seen through new eyes. These poems celebrate the sheer giddy delight of reading.

Girls and women in the past were frequently denied unfettered access to literature and education, and it is heartbreaking that, in some places in today's world, they are still struggling for equal opportunities. Here Sarah Egerton, writing in the early 1700s, launches a blistering manifesto in 'The Emulation' inciting women to take up space in the literary world, and Diane Glancy, Audre Lorde and Kate Tempest leave us in no doubt that words can break down walls.

In a Cardiff Arcade, 1952

One of those little shops too small
for the worlds they hold, where words
that sing you to sleep, stories
that stalk your dreams,
open like golden windows in a wall.

One small room leads to another,
the first bright-windowed on the street,
alluring, luminous. The other is dusk,
walled with pressed pages, old books
with leathery breath and freckled leaves.

What stays is not the book alone
but where you took it down,
how it felt in your hands,
how she wrapped it in brown paper,
how you carried it home,

how it holds wild seas
that knock the earth apart,
how words burn, freeze,
to break and heal your heart.

Gillian Clarke

Sonnet XXXI

Oh, oh, you will be sorry for that word!
Give back my book and take my kiss instead.
Was it my enemy or my friend I heard,
'What a big book for such a little head!'
Come, I will show you now my newest hat,
And you may watch me purse my mouth and prink!
Oh, I shall love you still, and all of that.
I never again shall tell you what I think.
I shall be sweet and crafty, soft and sly;
You will not catch me reading any more:
I shall be called a wife to pattern by;
And some day when you knock and push the door,
Some sane day, not too bright and not too stormy,
I shall be gone, and you may whistle for me.

Edna St Vincent Millay

from Aurora Leigh

Books, books, books!
I had found the secret of a garret-room
Piled high with cases in my father's name;
Piled high, packed large, – where, creeping in and out
Among the giant fossils of my past,
Like some small nimble mouse between the ribs
Of a mastodon, I nibbled here and there
At this or that box, pulling through the gap,
In heats of terror, haste, victorious joy,
The first book first. And how I felt it beat
Under my pillow, in the morning's dark,
An hour before the sun would let me read!
My books! At last, because the time was ripe,
I chanced upon the poets.
                            As the earth
Plunges in fury, when the internal fires
Have reached and pricked her heart, and, throwing flat
The marts and temples, the triumphal gates
And towers of observation, clears herself
To elemental freedom – thus, my soul,
At poetry's divine first finger touch,
Let go conventions and sprang up surprised,
Convicted of the great eternities
Before two worlds.

Elizabeth Barrett Browning

Books
after Larkin

If I were called in
to construct a religion
I should make use of books.

Going to church
would entail a bracing traipse
through make-believe woods.

My liturgy would employ
a splendour of lamplight
and the hush-hush of pages at dusk.

And I should be the old
factotum of books,
bent to the beautiful spines
and mouthing the words like a moth.

Katharine Towers

Poem

In the earnest path of duty,
    With the high hopes and hearts sincere,
We, to useful lives aspiring,
    Daily meet to labor here.

No vain dreams of earthly glory
    Urge us onward to explore
Far-extending realms of knowledge,
    With their rich and varied store;

But, with hope of aiding others,
    Gladly we perform our part;
Nor forget, the mind, while storing,
    We must educate the heart, —

Teach it hatred of oppression,
    Truest love of God and man;
Thus our high and holy calling
    May accomplish His great plan.

Not the great and gifted only
    He appoints to do his will.
But each one, however lowly,
    Has a mission to fulfill.

Knowing this, toil we unwearied,
   With true hearts and purpose high; –
We would win a wreath immortal
   Whose bright flowers ne'er fade and die.

Charlotte L. Forten Grimké

from The Emulation

They fear we should excel their sluggish parts,
Should we attempt the sciences and arts;
Pretend they were designed for them alone,
So keep us fools to raise their own renown.
Thus priests of old, their grandeur to maintain,
Cried vulgar eyes would sacred laws profane;
So kept the mysteries behind a screen:
Their homage and the name were lost had they been seen.
But in this blessèd age such freedom's given,
That every man explains the will of heaven;
And shall we women now sit tamely by,
Make no excursions in philosophy,
Or grace our thoughts in tuneful poetry?
We will our rights in learning's world maintain;
Wit's empire now shall know a female reign.
Come, all ye fair, the great attempt improve,
Divinely imitate the realms above:
There's ten celestial females govern wit,
And but two gods that dare pretend to it.
And shall these finite males reverse their rules?
No, we'll be wits, and then men must be fools.

Sarah Egerton

we misread 'language' as 'lavender'

gather symbols and sounds from the garden,
rub the buds between palms,
let it sit and dry before use.

distil oils from homegrown morphemes,
let them sooth the hurts, the burns

scoop a mantra into muslin sachets,
tuck into the skull's dark corners
to quiet the moths.

when nights are bad neighbourhoods
and dawn is not home,
scatter lexemes under your pillow.
let a story grow
and dream into it.
In the morning,
keep breathing. It'll be there.

watch phrases buzz, drowsy,
scent-drunk, until something catches and
clings on, holding faith in fragile things.

Christy Ku

Poem

A poem stays awake long after midnight
talking you from room to room,

does not care that walls have ears,
las paredes oyen

A poem prefers tin to silver,
silver to gold,
gold to platinum

Every year
a poem tosses a young woman from the cliffs
to the rocky sea below

A poem accidentally sends the entire letter f
off to Florence

but keeps the letter t
in a matchbox, like a tiny contraband tortoise

Sometimes
a poem is your only daughter

busy and happy in the world,
China or Spain,
abundancia de riqueza

Like the partial Angel Gabriel
in Santa Sophia
a poem is a half-god, half-invisible

A poem will do things in England
she'll never do in France

It will take more than the ten thousand lakes
for which Minnesota is famous
to drown a poem

The poem pauses now and then
to look at nothing-much-in-particular

A poem likes scraping and burnishing
the prepared surface of the copper,

is frequently found note-taking copiously
from *The Fantastic Historia Animalium of the Rain*

A poem makes herself tiny as a waterbear
or a tardygrade,
a mite able to survive freezing, boiling

able to go into suspended animation
for one hundred years, if need be.

Penelope Shuttle

Kemo Sabe

In my dream I take the white man
slap him til he loves me.
I tie him to the house,
take his land & buffalo.
I put other words into his mouth,
words he doesn't understand
like spoonfuls of smashed lima beans
until his cheeks bulge.
Chew now, dear, I say.
I flick his throat until he swallows.
He works all day,
never leaves the house.
The floors shine,
the sheets are starched.
He wipes grime from the windows
until clouds dance across the glass.
He feeds me when I'm hungry.
I can leave whenever I want.
Let him struggle for his dignity,
this time let him remember
my name.

Diane Glancy

When to Write

When your fists are ready to paint faces
When there is nowhere to confide
When your skin lingers high above your bones
and you're so out of touch with self,
Write.
When the mouth fails you
and shyness strangles
and your throat becomes tight,
Write.
When your eyes won't dry,
Write.
Before your fight
Before you fall,
Write.
When they lie to you
When they hurt you
When they leave you,
Write.
And if they return,
And they have listened
You better write.
When the urge arises
Step out of the shower
And write.
When the world denies you
Find you power
And write.
When they speak of a freedom that doesn't include you . . .

Write away those bars
Write together your scars
Write around your wounds
Write into your womb
Write upwards
Write inwards
Write through and write around
Absolutely everything that tries to steal your sound.

Sophia Thakur

The cypher

A circle. Shoulders and hard chests and arms like rosary beads
from push-ups before bed, eyes narrowed.
We wear our hoods up. We talk in couplets.
Two lines at a time and my heart has
never been calmer than here,
in the cypher.

I stare at my trainers and listen to deep voices
throwing out lyrics through smoke.
I know I can do this much better than them.
I can feel it. Something like stillness,
but nothing like stillness.

It creeps up my throat like water creeps down it.
It spreads itself over my tongue.
My shoulders are squared.
I move like the boys,
I talk like the boys,
but my words are my own.

And when I unleash them, my eyes widen and focus.
The streetlights stop flickering, just for a moment,
the arrogance prickles like sweat at my temples,
I'm moving as if I have never been gentle.
The kinder among them look at me sideways.
Smiling, shaking their heads,
I feel it all through me.
It's shaking my legs.

I push my fist against theirs, my soft arms are clasped,
I'm embraced like a man, my back slapped,
and my heart all the time getting faster.
The beatboxer nods his respect.
And I'm feeling bigger than
all of those buildings.
I wait for my turn again,
everything burning.

Kate Tempest

Coal

I
Is the total black, being spoken
From the earth's inside.
There are many kinds of open.
How a diamond comes into a knot of flame
How a sound comes into a word, coloured
By who pays what for speaking.

Some words are open
Like a diamond on glass windows
Singing out within the crash of passing sun
Then there are words like stapled wagers
In a perforated book – buy and sign and tear apart –
And come whatever wills all chances
The stub remains
An ill-pulled tooth with a ragged edge.
Some words live in my throat
Breeding like adders. Others know sun
Seeking like gypsies over my tongue
To explode through my lips
Like young sparrows bursting from shell.
Some words
Bedevil me.

Love is a word another kind of open —
As a diamond comes into a knot of flame
I am black because I come from the earth's inside
Take my word for jewel in your open light.

Audre Lorde

Wings
(for Miss)

Under her wings I live and grow and against
and with the feathers soft and
strong that open over
the heads of all who
reach up guiding
up
and
out
until the wings
flutter away and we
who are not in need grow
wings for ourselves and open
them up to those without wings

Ellie Steel

from Washing Day

At intervals my mother's voice was heard,
Urging dispatch: briskly the work went on,
All hands employed to wash, to rinse, to wring,
To fold, and starch, and clap, and iron, and plait.
Then would I sit me down, and ponder much
Why washings were. Sometimes through hollow bowl
Of pipe amused we blew, and sent aloft
The floating bubbles; little dreaming then
To see, Montgolfier, thy silken ball
Ride buoyant through the clouds, so near approach
The sports of children and the toils of men.
Earth, air, and sky, and ocean, hath its bubbles,
And verse is one of them – this most of all.

Anna Laetitia Barbauld

'My wild hair backward blown' – Taking Flight

A poem can lift us up. These poets sweep us skywards, to feel the magnificent power of a wind that can 'tear at the pillars of the world' or gently ruffle a sick child's nursery curtains. With Anna Hempstead Branch, we straddle a broomstick to ride the wind – 'wild, dangerous and holy' – with her fierce coven.

Vanessa Kisuule reminds us that flight of all kinds is real-world magic, and Beatrice Gibbs lets us limp home with the boys in a scarred but miraculously spared bomber. Poets have always understood that there will always be days when we long, like Colette Bryce's narrator, to scale a rope that stretches into the sky and vanish, somewhere up there.

The Destroyer

I am of the wind . . .
A wisp of the battering wind . . .

I trail my fingers along the Alps
And an avalanche falls in my wake . . .
I feel in my quivering length
When it buries the hamlet beneath . . .

I hurriedly sweep aside
The cities that clutter our path . . .
As we whirl about the circle of the globe . . .
As we tear at the pillars of the world . . .
Open to the wind,
The Destroyer!
The wind that is battering at your gates.

Lola Ridge

Flying to Italy

The Alps are a college of grand-
mothers in white caps. Massed
profiles rear up, as pure
as nuns'.

They dandle only the air
on their scalloped laps.
Clouds infiltrate
their knees' blue valleys.

Closer they are all
mouth: discussing
the clatter of pilots out of tin
carrycots onto these ridged tips
that snap them up, teeth
needling the lovely boys, tongues
sucking the gristle off bones.

You could easily lose your heart
to these bad grannies:
they are so possessive!

They'll cherish
the flesh of businessmen
better than any hostess, these
lipsmacking sisters; they'll
teach young wives and other
survivors how to carve up
the sun-dried dead, and eat.

We scuttle past.
Now we're only a glint
in their turquoise eye.

Patience is their vocation.

Michèle Roberts

holiday

on a crack of dawn flight
to another country, another tongue
and another culture
you are tired of the crick in your neck
the press of the seat in front of your knees

you want to be stationary
greeted by the same view from your window
for at least three consecutive days

but when you land
you are met with the joy
of unfamiliar streets and universal customs
a myriad of words for *hello, thank you* and *sorry*
are brief guests in your bashful mouth

as you walk round a grand fountain
framed in the dazzling green only
the utopia of scandinavia could offer
a conversation with an aunt
floats to the top of your mind

one in which she confided
she had never left her country
that all her other siblings had
never even left their village

and it's all you can do
not to weep in the face of chance
and its callous scattergun hand
you vow to never take the miracle
of flight for granted again
but the tears do not stop

a kind fair-haired man stops
to survey the scene of you
and before you can look away
he asks in improbably perfect english
if there's anything he can do
to help you

Vanessa Kisuule

The Bomber

White moon setting and red sun waking,
    White as a searchlight, red as a flame,
Through the dawn wind her hard way making,
    Rhythmless, riddled, the bomber came.

Men who had thought their last flight over,
    All hoping gone, came limping back,
Marvelling, looked on bomb-scarred Dover,
    Buttercup fields and white Down track.

Cottage and ploughland, green lanes weaving,
    Working-folk stopping to stare overhead –
Lovely, most lovely, past all believing
    To eyes of men new-raised from the dead.

Beatrice R. Gibbs

Hungary

Look,
At these flat lands
Before you. Endless sky
Fills empty space.
Stand here,
And open up your mind.
Notice the light
Riding on its cloud horse
Throwing shadows
On the grassy ground.
Stand here
And hear the whistle of the wind
Blowing the golden sand.
Remember it,
Elsewhere,
The free and wild wind,

As a gentle touch.

Vivien Urban

Spring Wind in London

I blow across the stagnant world,
I blow across the sea,
For me, the sailor's flag unfurled,
For me, the uprooted tree.
My challenge to the world is hurled;
The world must bow to me.

I drive the clouds across the sky,
I huddle them like sheep,
Merciless shepherd's dog am I
And shepherd's watch I keep.
If in the quiet vales they lie
I blow them up the steep.

Lo! In the tree-tops do I hide,
In every living thing;
On the moon's yellow wings I glide,
On the wild rose I swing;
On the sea-horse's back I ride,
And what then do I bring?

And when a little child is ill
I pause, and with my hand
I wave the window curtain's frill
That he may understand
Outside the wind is blowing still;
. . . It is a pleasant land.

Oh, stranger in a foreign place,
See what I bring to you.
This rain — is tears upon your face;
I tell you — tell you true
I came from that forgotten place
Where once the wattle grew.

All the wild sweetness of the flower
Tangled against the wall.
It was that magic, silent hour . . .
The branches grew so tall
They twined themselves into a bower.
The sun shone . . . and the fall

Of yellow blossom on the grass!
You feel that golden rain?
Both of you could not hold, alas,
Both of you tried — in vain.
A memory, stranger. So I pass . . .
It will not come again.

Katherine Mansfield

from Sonnets from a Lock Box

XXV

Into the void behold my shuddering flight,
Plunging straight forward through unhuman space,
My wild hair backward blown and my white face
Set like a wedge of ice. My chattering teeth
Cut like sharp knives my swiftly freezing breath.
Perched upon straightness I seek a wilder zone.
My Flying Self – on this black steed alone –
Drives out to God or else to utter death.
Beware straight lines which do subdue man's pride!
'Tis on a broomstick that great witches ride.
Wild, dangerous and holy are the runes
Which shift the whirling atoms with their tunes.
Oh like a witch accursed shall she be burned
Who having flown on straightness has returned.

Anna Hempstead Branch

The Full Indian Rope Trick

There was no secret
murmured down through a long line
of elect; no dark fakir, no flutter
of notes from a pipe,
no proof, no footage of it —
but I did it,

Guildhall Square, noon,
in front of everyone.
There were walls, bells, passers-by;
then a rope, thrown, caught by the sky
and me, young, up and away,
goodbye.

Goodbye, goodbye.
Thin air. First try.
A crowd hushed, squinting eyes
at a full sun. There
on the stones
the slack weight of a rope

coiled in a crate, a braid
eighteen summers long,
and me
I'm long gone,
my one-off trick
unique, unequalled since.

And what would I tell them
given the chance?
It was painful; it took years.
I'm my own witness,
guardian of the fact
that I'm still here.

Colette Bryce

On the South Downs

Over the downs there were birds flying,
        Far off glittered the sea,
And toward the north the weald of Sussex
        Lay like a kingdom under me.

I was happier than the larks
        That nest on the downs and sing to the sky —
Over the downs the birds flying
        Were not so happy as I.

It was not you, though you were near,
        Though you were good to hear and see,
It was not earth, it was not heaven,
        It was myself that sang in me.

Sara Teasdale

'It's better with all the banners flying' – Courage, Hope and Resilience

These are brave verses. Ella May Wiggins, an Appalachian mill-worker supporting her large family, organized against her exploitative employers using words as weapons in a struggle that cost her her life. As well as anger, there is astonishing joy and hope in her poetry. Here are gathered passionate words of activism, songs for suffragettes and crumbs of comfort for the disappointed.

War poems are not all by Tommies in the trenches. Thyrza Leyshon gives us Edith Sitwell, bejewelled and unflinching, declaiming poetry unconcernedly as the Blitz rages. Jan Dean imagines the perilous journey of Gladys Aylward, a missionary who led the orphans in her care to safety along mountain paths when Yangcheng in China was bombed in 1938. Daring and hope are vital ingredients when mixing up a new world, and these lines promise us that our courage will not fail.

'Out of the darkness'

Out of the darkness
on a dark path,
I now set out.
Shine on me,
moon of the mountain edge.

Izumi Shikibu

Translated by Kenneth Rexroth
and Ikuko Atsumi

Miss Aylward's Journey

Now that clouds have covered up the moon
the mountain's black,
one hundred children huddle in the rocks
like sleeping sheep

and I'm their shepherd
on this long hard haul,
higher and higher by sharp crags,
creep-clinging
on the lips of deep ravines.

Escaping from the soldiers,
who have overrun Yangcheng,
now in this barren place
it seems to me
that we have leapt
from frying pan to fire.
I keep watch for wolves
And men with guns.

After twelve days walking
we reach the Yellow River.
There is no way to cross.

We kneel here
And pray for help.
We sing.
God's ears that day
Are on a Chinese officer,
Who hears us,
rides over, sees our difficulty,
and solves it with a boat.

In the city of Sian
there's safe haven
for us all. The children fall
into real beds,
and I fall into fever –
delirium
of terrifying journeys,
rockfalls, raging rivers,
dangers in the darkness
of the hidden moon.

Jan Dean

Sangharsh Karna Hai

here, the hurried truth:
day after day after day
of battling death and
keeping him at bay
you became the star
taking struggle in her stride
and we became the body
breaking free, we became
the scream cutting loose
from the curse of silence,
we became the protest
that poured like blood
from a wounded night
and learning from you,
we became the flesh
that became the fight.

Meena Kandasamy

All Around the Jailhouse

All around the jailhouse
Waiting for a trial;
One mile from the union hall
Sleeping in the jail.
I walked up to the policeman
To show him I had no fear;
He said, 'If you've got money
I'll see that you don't stay here.'

'I haven't got a nickel,
Not a penny can I show.'
'Lock her up in the cell,' he said,
As he slammed the jailhouse door.
He let me out in July,
The month I dearly love;
The wide open spaces all around me,
The moon and stars above.

Everybody seems to want me,
Everybody but the scabs.
I'm on my way from the jailhouse,
I'm going back to the union hall.
Though my tent now is empty
My heart is full of joy;
I'm a mile away from the union hall,
Just a-waiting for a strike.

Ella May Wiggins

Locked Inside

She beats upon her bolted door,
    With faint weak hands;
Drearily walks the narrow floor;
Sullenly sits, blank walls before;
    Despairing stands.

Life calls her, Duty, Pleasure, Gain –
    Her dreams respond;
But the blank daylights wax and wane,
Dull peace, sharp agony, slow pain –
    No hope beyond.

Till she comes a thought! She lifts her head,
    The world grows wide!
A voice – as if clear words were said –
'Your door, O long imprisonéd,
    Is locked inside!'

Charlotte Perkins Gilman

L'Envoi

Stepping onwards, oh, my comrades!
Marching fearless through the darkness,
Marching fearless through the prisons,
With the torch of freedom guiding!

See the face of each is glowing,
Gleaming with the love of freedom;
Gleaming with a selfless triumph,
In the cause of human progress!

Like the pilgrim in the valley,
Enemies may oft assail us,
Enemies may close around us,
Tyrants, hunger, horror, brute-force.

But the glorious dawn is breaking,
Freedom's beauty sheds her radiance;
Freedom's clarion call is sounding,
Rousing all the world to wisdom.

Emily Wilding Davison

December

Hope in jars, it lines the shelves.
We hug it close to warm ourselves.

It's admirable to cling to hope –
protest, protect, go out and vote.

And when, in the morning light,
this hope of ours does not shine bright,

we coax it back.
We mourn.

We fight.

Jen Campbell

New Glass

We hold up the new gods of our post-electric reality.

Echo our dreams into empty rooms,
shelter the strange television flowers that try to seduce
us away from the memory of weather.

But outside there is new rain. Twenty-five sets of hands
to make you feel at home.

When you close your eyes, you hear the sound of wind
trapped behind the police station like a sacrifice.

You think back to all the homes you once sold yourself,
the eyes behind the hotel windows, facing out on a cold
Euston station.

How you live further than trying to sleep now.

The kingdom is in recess,

we have built love a blanket and put sticks in it like a tent,

we have let the land own it and protect the people who find it.

We tell their stories, choir the threads of it, make friends
with the birds who fly in and out of the Wi-Fi signals.

We sing new wonder at our collective hope, and make new glass from it.

Greta Bellamacina

Release

With swift
Great sweep of her
Magnificent arm my pain
Clanged back the doors that shut my soul
From life.

Adelaide Crapsey

Her Kind

I have gone out, a possessed witch,
haunting the black air, braver at night;
dreaming evil, I have done my hitch
over the plain houses, light by light:
lonely thing, twelve-fingered, out of mind.
A woman like that is not a woman, quite.
I have been her kind.

I have found the warm caves in the woods,
filled them with skillets, carvings, shelves,
closets, silks, innumerable goods;
fixed the suppers for the worms and the elves:
whining, rearranging the disaligned.
A woman like that is misunderstood.
I have been her kind.

I have ridden in your cart, driver,
waved my nude arms at villages going by,
learning the last bright routes, survivor
where your flames still bite my thigh
and my ribs crack where your wheels wind.
A woman like that is not ashamed to die.
I have been her kind.

Anne Sexton

The Lady with the Sewing-Machine

Across the fields as green as spinach,
Cropped as close as Time to Greenwich,

Stands a high house; if at all,
Spring comes like a Paisley shawl –

Patternings meticulous
And youthfully ridiculous.

In each room the yellow sun
Shakes like a canary, run

On run, roulade, and watery trill –
Yellow, meaningless, and shrill.

Face as white as any clock's,
Cased in parsley-dark curled locks –

All day long you sit and sew,
Stitch life down for fear it grow,

Stitch life down for fear we guess
At the hidden ugliness.

Dusty voice that throbs with heat,
Hoping with your steel-thin beat

To put stitches in my mind,
Make it tidy, make it kind,

You shall not: I'll keep it free
Though you turn earth, sky and sea

To a patchwork quilt to keep
Your mind snug and warm in sleep!

Edith Sitwell

Edith Sitwell

is fastening the gold collar made,
she says, *by one of my greatest friends,*
though I only met her once.
It has three pendulum blades, the largest
reaching from breast to breast.
She is taking a risk because it clanks
when reciting her poems. Tonight
she will take to The Churchill Club
a new poem, *Heart and Mind*.
It twitches among her manuscripts.

She holds her poem in jewelled fingers,
beams of light flash like searchlights finding
razor sharp partings in the hair of young soldiers.
She explains: *I've got such a dreadful cold*
and launches into *Still Falls the Rain*,
ignoring the sirens heralding an air raid.
Edith has always said of life: *it's better*
with all the banners flying – isn't it?

Although she loves jewellery, metal was dangerous
during childhood. Parents instructed
that her uselessly aristocratic nose be trussed,
prongs clamped to her face to straighten
it, her curved spine treated by iron corsets
and braces. Her favourite role is Lady Macbeth.

A doodlebug comes roaring overhead
and Edith gets louder and louder, refusing
to be silenced by an insistent missile.

On the day she dies she will breakfast
on a double martini, with the salutation: *I'm dying,
but apart from that I'm alright.*

Thyrza Leyshon

War Girls

There's the girl who clips your ticket for the train,
    And the girl who speeds the lift from floor to floor,
There's the girl who does a milk-round in the rain,
    And the girl who calls for orders at your door.
        Strong, sensible, and fit,
        They're out to show their grit,
     And tackle jobs with energy and knack.
        No longer caged and penned up,
        They're going to keep their end up
Till the khaki soldier boys come marching back.

There's the motor girl who drives a heavy van,
    There's the butcher girl who brings your joint of meat,
There's the girl who cries 'All fares, please!' like a man,
    And the girl who whistles taxis up the street.
        Beneath each uniform
        Beats a heart that's soft and warm,
    Though of canny mother-wit they show no lack;
        But a solemn statement this is,
        They've no time for love and kisses
Till the khaki soldier boys come marching back.

Jessie Pope

Wood Song

Daughters, when they come
we will hide in the forest,
we'll cross the meadow
and the orchard,

their sifting rooms,
till we are deer in the woods –
the quick-footed hind
and her fawns –

and we'll slip through the thickets
or take the water's scentless course,
and follow the lichen
brightening north,

and I'll keep you warm
where we nest
beneath the bracken's
tangled roof,

and in the morning when we wake
we will move, move, move,
beneath the dark forgiving hand
of the clouds,

with the slightest weather
moving on,
and when our feet fall
they will fall like rain,

and there will be no catching us,
and no harm will come,
so keep close daughters
in the woods were we run,

for we are tracks in the dew
vanishing at dawn,
we are mist, we are rain
we are gone.

Fiona Benson

'Riches I hold in light esteem'

Riches I hold in light esteem
   And Love I laugh to scorn
And lust of Fame was but a dream
   That vanished with the morn –

And if I pray – the only prayer
   That moves my lips for me
Is – 'Leave the heart that now I bear
   'And give me liberty.'

Yes, as my swift days near their goal
   'Tis all that I implore –
Through life and death, a chainless soul
   With courage to endure!

Emily Brontë

I want to stand naked in the school hall

on the podium, mid assembly,
so my presence will be so overbearing no one can look away.
I want their eyes to burn into my skin, examine
its ripples and folds and the scar that digs it up
like a trench in Ypres.

I'd watch a few hundred jaws slowly unhinge,
drop down into a mass of O's, all directed
at my body, lopsided like the projector, its fluorescent beams
bouncing on my raw flesh, so each goosebump
would have its own time in the spotlight.

I want to raise my arms, outstretch my fingertips,
so everyone can see my hairy armpits and wonky tits,
my nipples erect with the cold of a hundred stark looks,
so they'd know, so they'd see, I'm not perfect
and in no way do I want to be. Then,

when I've got their attention, I want to read them a poem
through the head teacher's microphone, full blast
so that each naked syllable in each naked word,
spat from my naked throat, near bursts their eardrums.
Before they stand, frozen and agape, and file out.

Lauren Hollingsworth-Smith

130

'Chasing weightlessness' – The Final Frontier

From children gazing out of the bedroom window long after they should have been asleep, to poets imagining their ascent into distant galaxies, we have always dreamed of wandering among the stars and holidaying on far-flung planets. Here are incantations to take us there.

For most of us, poetry will be our best shot at space travel. Not so for Sally Ride, the first American woman in space and the first known LGBTQ astronaut. In her passionate poem, Laura Fairgrieve imagines her holding a class spellbound, filling them with the fire to 'run fast enough to crack your scabs'. She tells them (and us):

> I did not wait for outerspace to extend its arm to me,
> I thrust my face skyward.

I Had a Boat

I had a boat, and the boat had wings;
    And I did dream that we went a flying
Over the heads of queens and kings,
    Over the souls dead and dying,
Up among the stars and the great white rings,
    And where the Moon on her back is lying.

Mary Elizabeth Coleridge

from Darkness Music

The days grow and the stars cross over
And my wild bed turns slowly among the stars.

Muriel Rukeyser

The Moon at Knowle Hill

The moon was married last night
and nobody saw
dressed up in her ghostly dress
for the summer ball.

The stars shimmied in the sky
and danced a whirligig;
the moon vowed to be true
and lit up the corn-rigs.

She kissed the dark lips of the sky
Above the summer house
She in her pale white dress
swooned across the vast sky

The moon was married last night
the beautiful belle of the ball
and nobody saw her at all
except a small girl in a navy dress

who witnessed it all.

Jackie Kay

'On the road through the clouds'

On the road through the clouds
Is there a short cut
To the summer moon?

Den Sute-Jo

*Translated by Kenneth Rexroth
and Ikuko Atsumi*

The Crescent Moon

Slipping softly through the sky
    Little horned, happy moon,
Can you hear me up so high?
    Will you come down soon?

On my nursery window-sill
    Will you stay your steady flight?
And then float away with me
    Through the summer night?

Brushing over tops of trees,
    Playing hide and seek with stars,
Peeping up through shiny clouds
    At Jupiter or Mars.

I shall fill my lap with roses
    Gathered in the milky way,
All to carry home to mother.
    Oh! what will she say!

Little rocking, sailing moon,
    Do you hear me shout – Ahoy!
Just a little nearer, moon,
    To please a little boy.

Amy Lowell

Sally Ride Speaks to the Schoolgirls

Don't believe the quiet heat that waits to pull
your velocipede to pieces
when you pedal like you're tired of waiting.
Someone will want to solder your throat shut
while your mind turns figure-eights around
faceless people who promise you
space travel is one hundred years away.
Do not close your mouth for them.
Speed comes to anti-gravity paint
the hacked up remains
of spoiled shoe laces and band-aids
that stew on the blacktops, awaiting no rescue.
Run fast enough to crack your scabs,
run fast enough to hear
your arteries turn all your thoughts to nothing
more than a righteous racket.
When I flew to the edge I was neither sight nor
sound, not a grayscale photo
I was speed
I was the hand that holds the storybook illustration
I airbrushed the shadows clean off the page
I was an acrobat courting the cold-blooded stars
I was the slingshot that pulls itself impossibly taut,
that kisses its spine good-bye.
I counted backwards and my bones became hollow
I steered the shuttle with no space for pins or needles
sometimes chasing weightlessness is the only way
to keep your blood blitzing, to remember the

years you spent writing out equations,
whispering promises to cramped book spines,
answering barbed questions, remembering
you're the first
and sitting up straighter.
I raced against the rest with
no sir, not a single tear shed
Danny Dunn turned anti-gravity cartwheels in my dreams
and there was no divide
my interstellar medium, X-ray visions and Canadarm arm
shot me straight up
I did not wait for outerspace to extend its arm to me,
I thrust my face skyward
where no tinted glass could have spared me
where a breathless canvas of black beckoned me close
where I offered my ear, I reached out my matte limbed
    machine
and snatched a shuttle whole
where the sun would have happily frozen me to death
if I drifted too close.

Laura Fairgrieve

Target

Aim higher than the clod of mud,
the thud in earth that's swallowed up,

the belly of a rusted can,
the clang of tin, unbalancing,

snails that cling to low flint walls,
the cracking of a hollow shell,

the plum upon a neighbour's tree,
a hush disturbed within its leaves,

and higher still than startled crows,
slanted attic windows, rows

of chimney stacks, church spires,
tower blocks. Aim higher.

Set sight between the blazing past
and unlit future of a star.

Aim now.

Rachel Rooney

De Profundis

Oh why is heaven built so far,
Oh why is earth set so remote?
I cannot reach the nearest star
That hangs afloat.

I would not care to reach the moon,
One round monotonous of change;
Yet even she repeats her tune
Beyond my range.

I never watch the scatter'd fire
Of stars, or sun's far-trailing train,
But all my heart is one desire,
And all in vain:

For I am bound with fleshly bands,
Joy, beauty, lie beyond my scope;
I strain my heart, I stretch my hands,
And catch at hope.

Christina Rossetti

Sky Ladder
after Cai Guo-Qiang

Quick, before the sun
rises, get up one more
time, my grandmother.
The artist won't mind
if you borrow
his sky ladder.
Place your foot
on the bottom rung
and keep climbing,
even though
you're a skeleton
with a broken neck
from falling downstairs
on Guy Fawkes night.
The ladder is wrapped
in gunpowder, and he's
lit the touchpaper.
Your bones are ascending
firecrackers.
You're half a kilometer
high now, halfway
to the universe,
my joy-gardener.
I hope you find a
garden with rich black
soil for your black

roses, hybrids like you —
half white half Indian,
half woman half flower,
their roots twined
through your skull,
you who were transplanted
among the pale roses
of a British family.
Your skin now a mix
of photons and soot.
What do you find up there?
Is there a hothouse?
Are there alien hands
with deft brushes
pollinating stars?
Remember how
your tomatoes kept
yielding more planets?
Are there constellations
of exotic fruit now
you've reached the top?
Have you gone back
enough in space-time
to when you were alive?
The ladder is charred,
the hot air balloon
that held it up
is about to collapse.
The explosions are over.

Cai showers his head
with champagne, as his
100-year-old granny
watches on her cell phone.
Did you see it? He asks,
did you hear the whoosh,
the rat-tat-tat
at the starry door?
You can go back
to sleep now, he tells her.
Go back to sleep,
I tell you, but first,
if you're hungry,
have a snack on one
of those quasars,
before you dream again
of the tumble
through air to
the stone landing,
fireworks the last
thing you hear.

Pascale Petit

Devil at the End of Love

Surprised at the birth of stars,
passions built on noble gases,
the Devil objects. An Angel comes
full of light and carbon compounds
to chase him off with promise,
possibility lit in a single word.
Devil says WIE HEIßT DAS WORT?
and the Angel laughs into infinity.
'Do you not know the only Word?
the Word that wings joyfully
through the universe? The Word
that expiates all guilt, the eternal
Word?' Now is the time for violins,
morsing out in bold metallic bursts
as hands are held, silences broken.
Devil says WIE HEIßT DAS WORT
and there is a solid flash of horizon,
as hearts explode in unending
strokes, a complete understanding
of ourselves. Joy. Flashes of light.
    The singular reality tonight:

\|||||||/
– L I E B E –
/|||||||\

Chrissy Williams

The Hubble Space Telescope before repair

The way they tell it
All the stars have wings
The sky so full of wings
There is no sky
And just for a moment
You forget
The error and the crimped
Paths of light
And you see it
The immense migration
And you hear the rush
The beating

Rebecca Elson

Avowal

Once and for all, I go my chosen way,
Once and for all, neglect to interfere.
Upon the very forehead of the day
I set my seal, and dare to persevere
In making pit and pinnacle my own,
In staying – at what cost! – natively free;
In meeting, unmolested and alone,
What is, and was, and presently will be.

Through this ungovernable air between the dark
Of comets' paths, I cut a glittering arc,
Dying as I was born, an original spark,
Orbitless, golden, answering to none,
Conditioned in myself, ended, begun
And ended, with the shrivelling of the sun.

Virginia Moore

'It's the sea I want' – Voyages by Verse

It isn't usually girls, in the old stories, who run away to sea. But who can smell the salt, or taste the spray, and not long to set sail? We need new stories. This chapter begins on the seashore, with Moya Cannon's tethered boats straining, as we do, at their moorings. We plunge into the waves or board boats to strike out for destinations unknown, for places rich and strange. There is something about the sea that whispers or roars at us, as Edith Södergran writes, that 'the saga can happen, even to you'.

Sabrina Mahfouz and Emma Lazarus, writing over a century apart, also remind us of 'the homeless, the tempest-tost', and the hope that those fleeing across the waves will find freedom and a safe harbour where they make land.

Hunter's Moon

There are perhaps no accidents,
no coincidences.
When we stumble against people, books, rare moments out
of time,
these are illuminations —
like the hunter's moon that sails tonight in its high clouds,
casting light into our black harbour,
where four black turf boats
tug at their ropes,
hunger for the islands.

Moya Cannon

Strawberries and the Sailing Ship

We sat on the top of the cliff
Overlooking the open sea
Our backs turned to the little town
Each of us had a basket of strawberries
We had just bought them from a dark woman
With quick eyes – berry-finding eyes
They're fresh picked said she from our own garden
The tips of her fingers were stained a bright red!
Heavens what strawberries
Each one was the finest
The perfect berry – the strawberry Absolute
The fruit of our childhood!
The very air came fanning
On strawberry wings
And down below, in the pools
Little children were bathing
With strawberry faces.
Over the blue swinging water
A three masted sailing ship
With nine ten eleven sails
Wonderfully beautifully!
She came riding
As though every sail were taking its fill
of the sun and the light.
And Oh! how I'd love to be on board said Anne.
The captain was below, but the crew lay about
Idle and handsome –

Have some strawberries we said
Slipping and sliding on the polished decks
And shaking the baskets.

Katherine Mansfield

The Sea-Shore

I should like to dwell where the deep blue sea
Rock'd to and fro as tranquilly,
As if it were willing the halcyon's nest
Should shelter through summer its beautiful guest.
When a plaining murmur like that of a song,
And a silvery line come the waves along:
Now bathing – now leaving the gentle shore,
Where shining sea-shells lay scattered o'er.

And children wandering along the strand,
With the eager eye and the busy hand,
Heaping the pebbles and green sea-weed,
Like treasures laid up for a time of need.
Or tempting the waves with their daring feet,
To launch, perhaps, some tiny fleet:
Mimicking those which bear afar
The wealth of trade – and the strength of war.

I should love, when the sun-set reddened the foam,
To watch the fisherman's boat come home,
With his well-filled net and glittering spoil:
Well has the noon-tide repaid its toil.
While the ships that lie in the distance away
Catch on their canvas the crimsoning ray,
Like fairy ships in the tales of old,
When the sails they spread were purple and gold.

Then the deep delight of the starry night,
With its shadowy depths and dreamy light:
When far away spreads the boundless sea,
As if it imagined infinity.
Let me hear the winds go singing by,
Lulling the waves with their melody:
While the moon like a mother watches their sleep,
And I ask no home but beside the deep.

Letitia Elizabeth Landon

It's the Sea I Want

It's the sea I want,
Make no mistake,
Not the resorts
With boardinghouses
Pressed together and shivering,
Praying for sun
And central heating –
It's the sea I want,
The whole boiling,
Destructive, disruptive, sterilising –
I think it's smashing

Undermining
This island,
Unpinning
Gorse and headland,
Arresting, without warrant,
Growth and sunlight.
Landscapes at risk,
Thumped with fists of wind,
Eaten up with a mouthful of mist,
Slump like a Stock Market
Suddenly into the Channel.
Down the long final slide
Go houses full of the dying,
Carefully tended gardens
Into the riot of salt . . .

While
All along
A population of cold
Shelled and speechless creatures
Waits, to inherit
The hot, hideous, restless
Chaos I've helped to make
In sixty industrious years.
Sixy industrious years
And the motorway from the Midlands
Have brought me down at last
To the level of the sea.
I see with the sea's eye.

It bites the cliffs,
Fondles the coast, and swings
Away again, out to sea,
Waving, waving,
Making no promises,
It spits back in our faces
The coins and cans of the beaches.

It's the sea I want,
Belting the land, breaking
All the rules, speaking
Its guttural, thrusting tongue.
It pays no taxes,
Cringes before no conscience
And carries its own prestige
On its naked, shining back.

It's the sea I want,
If it's not too late
To sit, and contemplate
The hard bright barbarous jewels
Of the totally indifferent sea:
Something I never made
And cannot be guilty of.

I have done with the pains of love.
Leave me alone with the sea,
That picks bones clean,
And was, and shall be.

Elma Mitchell

Dare

Yesterday, I breasted
the Atlantic while the day
stood by with held
breath shivering on
the cusp of autumn

the cliffs stretched
west as far as they dared.
I swam across the white
loosening noose of waves
a little further.

Kate Clanchy

Sea Love

Tide be runnin' the great world over:
   'Twas only last June month I mind that we
Was thinkin' the toss and the call in the breast of the lover
   So everlastin' as the sea.

Heer's the same little fishes that sputter and swim,
   Wi' the moon's old glim on the grey, wet sand;
An' him no more to me nor me to him
   Than the wind goin' over my hand.

Charlotte Mew

Staying in the Mountains in Summer

I've moved here to the Immortals' place:
Flowers everywhere we didn't plant before.

The courtyard trees are bent like clothes-horses.
At the feast, winecups float in a new spring.

Dark balcony. Path through deep bamboo.
Long summer dress. Confusion of books.

I sing in the moonlight and ride a painted boat,
Trusting the wind to blow me home again.

Yü Hsüan-chi

Translated by Geoffrey Waters

from Elegy on Captain Cook

Say first, what Power inspir'd his dauntless breast
With scorn of danger, and inglorious rest,
To quit imperial London's gorgeous domes,
Where, deck'd in thousand tints, bright Pleasure roams;
In cups of summer-ice her nectar pours,
Or twines, 'mid wint'ry snows, her roseate bowers . . .
Where Beauty moves with fascinating grace,
Calls the sweet blush to wanton o'er her face,
On each fond youth her soft artillery tries,
Aims her light smile, and rolls her frolic eyes:
What Power inspir'd his dauntless breast to brave
The scorch'd Equator, and th'Antarctic wave?

Anna Seward

Exultation is the going

Exultation is the going
Of an inland soul to sea,
Past the houses – past the headlands –
Into deep Eternity –

Bred as we, among the mountains,
Can the sailor understand
The divine intoxication
of the first league out from land?

Emily Dickinson

from Notes on the Voyage of Owl and Girl

// The Voyage

An owl and a girl most ['adventurous', 'curious', 'studious'] ['set out', 'set sail', 'sailed away'] in a ['bottle green', 'beetle-green', 'pea-green'] ['boat', 'sieve', 'skiff', 'vessel']; a ['beautiful', 'shipshape', 'sea worthy'] ['craft', 'raft', 'wooden shoe'], certainly, though a ['good deal', 'wee bit', 'tad'] too ['small', 'high in the stern'] to suit the two of them. They took a ['bushel', 'barrel', 'bundle'] of ['honey', 'money'] and an ['almanac', 'astrolabe', 'barometer', 'chronometer'] of dubious ['accuracy', 'origin', 'usefulness']. The owl was ['actually', 'basically', 'simply', 'slightly'] ['home sick', 'sea sick', 'sceptical', 'terrible with directions', 'a nervous traveller']. The girl sought to gain ['definitive', 'further', 'first-hand'] ['knowledge', 'experience', 'proof'] of ['the Northwest Passage', 'Ultima Thule', 'a strange phenomena known as sea lung'].

According to my ['calculations', 'library books', 'test results'], the girl informed the owl, it's ['six', 'seventeen', 'twenty-seven'] ['leagues', 'knots', 'nights', 'nautical miles'] ['due north', 'north', 'northeast'] of here. Her ['mother', 'great-aunt', 'grandmother'] had been among the most revered of ['authors', 'experts', 'philosophers'] on this topic. But the girl had her own ['life to live', 'line of inquiry', 'ideas', 'theories'].

The owl said, ['Birds of a feather stick together', 'Loose lips sink ships', 'Everywhere we go, there we are'].

How soon he ['drifted', 'floated', 'sailed', 'veered'] off ['topic', 'course', 'track', 'radar']!

According to my ['spyglass', 'sea chart', 'sextant', 'sonar'], we're nearing the edge of ['our story', 'our journey', 'the earth', 'this narrow sea'], the girl said, but still they sailed ['for a year and a day', 'on through the night', 'on until well past bed time'], ['despite the wet and sea fret', 'by the light of the silvery moon', 'across the North Atlantic', 'on a river of crystal light', 'into a sea of dew'].

By this time, all the owl's ['magazine subscriptions', 'snack food items', 'phone card credits', 'batteries'] had run out.

Don't ['fret', 'jinx us', 'obsess', 'second-guess'], said the girl most ['ardently', 'rationally', 'seriously']. The ['diaries', 'letters', 'lists', 'ships' logs'] she kept constitute the entirety of the ['knowledge', 'evidence', 'proof', 'records', 'traces'] we have left of this, ['impossible', 'implausible', 'improbable'] voyage toward ['the edge of the earth', the fountain of youth'].

J. R. Carpenter

Strange Sea

Implausible fish bloom in the depths,
mecurial flowers light up the coast;
I know red and yellow, the other colors—

But the sea, *det granna granna havet*, that's most dangerous
to look at.

What name is there for the color that arouses
this thirst, which says,
the saga can happen, even to you—

Edith Södergran

Translated by Averill Curdy

Saint Senara and Me

We're floating away in a barrel,
Princess Senara and me.

The malevolent King packed us in,
hurled us into the Celtic sea.

Selkies sing to us, porpoises guide us,
kittiwakes point the way.

Senara rows with her strong arms
and feeds me turtle tea.

She reads the stars, she whispers to waves,
she calms their swell and gyre.

She keeps me warm in her long red hair
tangled with langoustines.

We pitch and roll, I swallow the rain,
our barrel fills with minnows.

Senara grows gills and a silvery tail,
she swims us into tomorrow.

The Bay of Biscay is far away,
my toes touch shingle and shale.

I crawl onto the sand of this tin-rich land,
saved by my mermaid mother.

Anna Kisby

The Winds of Fate

One ship drives east and another drives west
With the selfsame winds that blow.
    'Tis the set of the sails
    And not of the gales
Which tells us the way to go.

Like the winds of the sea are the ways of fate,
As we voyage along through life;
    'Tis the set of a soul
    That decides its goal,
And not the calm or the strife.

Ella Wheeler Wilcox

Boats in a Storm

In response to Bakhuizen
ART UK Film

Look.
How does a painting capture
stillness in chaos?
Is it through the narrow range of grey
the refusal to smudge edges?
Or is it that in the wild but contrived waves
of a painted storm belongs our true future?
Frothy, merciless, cold –
we are seized.

There sit 287 people in Parliament
who'd replace humanity's complexity
with clear and simplified blocks of colour,
make children the distant background of a painting,
matt polish pushing salvageable suffering from sight.
They would have us nod in front of oil on canvas,
I agree, it's an extraordinary depiction
of a terrifying moment.
Applaud us to retreat into a disorder without detail,
the patient artifice of babels
bodies that are hardboiled,
awaiting the peeling.

Look.
A sun and steeple in the distance –
does the artist suggest we can be saved
from cauldron clouds and augmented oceans?
I think that will require more than sun and steeples,
more than ropes flung to shore,
More than sculptured outlines of what is 'right'.
It will require, simply, all of the people
to steady our boats in a storm.

Sabrina Mahfouz

The New Colossus

Not like the brazen giant of Greek fame,
With conquering limbs astride from land to land;
Here at our sea-washed, sunset gates shall stand
A mighty woman with a torch, whose flame
Is the imprisoned lightning, and her name
Mother of Exiles. From her beacon-hand
Glows world-wide welcome; her mild eyes command
The air-bridged harbor that twin cities frame.
'Keep, ancient lands, your storied pomp!' cries she
With silent lips. 'Give me your tired, your poor,
Your huddled masses yearning to breathe free,
The wretched refuse of your teeming shore.
Send these, the homeless, tempest-tost to me,
I lift my lamp beside the golden door!'

Emma Lazarus

Emigravit

With sails full set, the ship her anchor weighs.
Strange names shine out beneath her figure head.
What glad farewells with eager eyes are said!
What cheer for him who goes, and him who stays!
Fair skies, rich lands, new homes, and untried days
Some go to seek: the rest but wait instead,
Watching the way wherein their comrades led,
Until the next stanch ship her flag doth raise.
Who knows what myriad colonies there are
Of fairest fields, and rich, undreamed-of gains
Thick planted in the distant shining plains
Which we call sky because they lie so far?
Oh, write of me, not 'Died in bitter pains,'
But 'Emigrated to another star!'

Helen Hunt Jackson

'Dream me mermaid' – Flights of Fancy

These poems exult in the power of writers – and our own imaginations – to transport us far from the world we know. Within the pages of a book, without leaving the sofa, we can board a 'dreamland train' or mount a make-believe steed for pastures either new or fondly remembered. Stevie Smith is whisked to an early-morning island by her exuberantly plumed hat, entirely thwarting her mother's tedious plan concerning a 'young man', and sinks beneath a forlorn sea to a court served by cats. And just what *is* Gary doing in that dark wood?

Poets have always guided readers through the afterlife, and here are brand new maps. Or, within the space of a few lines, we can travel back – to before the beginning – and watch Nikki Giovanni in 'Ego Tripping' as she shakes the world into being. The possibilities are limitless.

In Your Mind

The other country, is it anticipated or half-remembered?
Its language is muffled by the rain which falls all afternoon
one autumn in England, and in your mind
you put aside your work and head for the airport
with a credit card and a warm coat you will leave
on the plane. The past fades like newsprint in the sun.

You know people there. Their faces are photographs
on the wrong side of your eyes. A beautiful boy
in the bar on the harbour serves you a drink — what? —
asks you if men could possibly land on the moon.
A moon like an orange drawn by a child. No.
Never. You watch it peel itself into the sea.

Sleep. The rasp of carpentry wakes you. On the wall,
a painting lost for thirty years renders the room yours.
Of course. You go to your job, right at the old hotel, left,
then left again. You love your job. Apt sounds
mark the passing of the hours. Seagulls. Bells. A flute
practising scales. You swap a coin for a fish on the way home.

Then suddenly you are lost but not lost, dawdling
on the blue bridge, watching six swans vanish
under your feet. The certainty of place turns on the lights
all over town, turns up the scent on the air. For a moment
you are there, in the other country, knowing its name.
And then a desk. A newspaper. A window. English rain.

Carol Ann Duffy

from On Imagination

Imagination! who can sing thy force?
Or who describe the swiftness of thy course?
Soaring through air to find the bright abode,
Th' empyreal place of the thund'ring God,
We on thy pinions can surpass the wind,
And leave the rolling universe behind:
From star to star the mental optics rove,
Measure the skies, and range the realms above.
There in one view we grasp the mighty whole,
Or with new worlds amaze th' unbounded soul.

Phillis Wheatley

The Centaur

The summer that I was ten —
Can it be there was only one
summer that I was ten? It must

have been a long one then —
each day I'd go out to choose
a fresh horse from my stable

which was a willow grove
down by the old canal.
I'd go on my two bare feet.

But when, with my brother's jack-knife,
I had cut me a long limber horse
with a good thick knob for a head,

and peeled him slick and clean
except a few leaves for the tail,
and cinched my brother's belt

around his head for a rein,
I'd straddle and canter him fast
up the grass bank to the path,

trot along in the lovely dust
that talcumed over his hoofs,
hiding my toes, and turning

his feet to swift half-moons.
The willow knob with the strap
jouncing between my thighs

was the pommel and yet the poll
of my nickering pony's head.
My head and my neck were mine,

yet they were shaped like a horse.
My hair flopped to the side
like the mane of a horse in the wind.

My forelock swung in my eyes,
my neck arched and I snorted.
I shied and skittered and reared,

stopped and raised my knees,
pawed at the ground and quivered.
My teeth bared as we wheeled

and swished through the dust again.
I was the horse and the rider,
and the leather I slapped to his rump

spanked my own behind.
Doubled, my two hoofs beat
a gallop along the bank,

the wind twanged in my mane,
my mouth squared to the bit.
And yet I sat on my steed

quiet, negligent riding,
my toes standing the stirrups,
my thighs hugging his ribs.

At a walk we drew up to the porch.
I tethered him to a paling.
Dismounting, I smoothed my skirt

and entered the dusky hall.
My feet on the clean linoleum
left ghostly toes in the hall.

Where have you been? said my mother.
Been riding, I said from the sink,
and filled me a glass of water.

What's that in your pocket? she said.
Just my knife. It weighted my pocket
and stretched my dress awry.

Go tie back your hair, said my mother,
and *Why Is your mouth all green?*
*Rob Roy, he pulled some clover
as we crossed the field*, I told her.

May Swenson

The Chatelaine

I have built one, so have you;
Paved with marble, domed with blue,
Battlement and ladies' bower,
Donjon keep and watchman's tower.

I have climbed, as you have done,
To the tower at set of sun –
Crying from its parlous height,
'Watchman, tell us of the night.'

I have stolen at midnight bell,
Like you, to the secret cell,
Shuddering at its charnel breath –
Left lockfast the spectre, Death.

I have used your lure to call
Choice guests to my golden hall:
Rarely welcome, rarely free
To my hospitality.

In a glow of rosy light
Hours, like minutes, take their flight –
As from you they fled away,
When, like you, I bade them stay.

Ah! the pretty flow of wit,
And the good hearts under it;
While the wheels of life go round
With a most melodious sound.

Not a vestige anywhere
Of our grim familiar, Care –
Roses! from the trees of yore
Blooming by the rivers four.

Not a jar, and not a fret;
Ecstasy and longing met.
But why should I thus define –
Is not your chateau like mine?

Scarcely were it strange to meet
In that magic realm so sweet,
So! I'll take this dreamland train
Bound for my chateau in Spain.

May Sinclair

Roads

I know a country laced with roads,
    They join the hills and they span the brooks,
They weave like a shuttle between broad fields,
    And slide discreetly through hidden nooks.
They are canopied like a Persian dome
    And carpeted with orient dyes.
They are myriad-voiced, and musical,
    And scented with happiest memories.
O Winding roads that I know so well,
    Every twist and turn, every hollow and hill!
They are set in my heart to a pulsing tune
    Gay as a honey-bee humming in June.
'T is the rhythmic beat of a horse's feet
    And the pattering paws of a sheep-dog bitch;
'T is the creaking trees, and the singing breeze,
    And the rustle of leaves in the road-side ditch.

A cow in a meadow shakes her bell
    And the notes cut sharp through the autumn air,
Each chattering brook bears a fleet of leaves
    Their cargo the rainbow, and just now where
The sun splashed bright on the road ahead
    A startled rabbit quivered and fled.

O Uphill roads and roads that dip down!
    You curl your sun-spattered length along,
And your march is beaten into a song
    By the softly ringing hoofs of a horse
And the panting breath of the dogs I love.
    The pageant of Autumn follows its course
And the blue sky of Autumn laughs above.

And the song and the country become as one,
    I see it as music, I hear it as light;
Prismatic and shimmering, trembling to tone,
    The land of desire, my soul's delight.
And always it beats in my listening ears
    With the gentle thud of a horse's stride,
With the swift-falling steps of many dogs,
    Following, following at my side.
O Roads that journey to fairyland!
    Radiant highways whose vistas gleam,
Leading me on, under crimson leaves,
    To the opaline gates of the Castles of Dream.

Amy Lowell

My Hat

Mother said if I wore this hat
I should be certain to get off with the right sort of chap
Well, look where I am now, on a desert island
With so far as I can see no one at hand
I know what has happened though I suppose Mother wouldn't
    see
This hat being so strong has completely run away with me
I had the feeling it was beginning to happen the moment I put
    it on
What a moment that was as I rose up, I rose up like a flying
    swan
As strong as a swan too, why see how far my hat has flown
    me away
It took us a night to come and then a night and a day
And all the time the swan wing in my hat waved beautifully
Ah, I thought, How this hat becomes me.
First the sea was dark but then it was pale blue
And still the wing beat and we flew and we flew
A night and a day and a night, and by the old right way
Between the sun and the moon we flew until morning day.
It is always early morning here on this peculiar island
The green grass grows into the sea on the dipping land
Am I glad I am here? Yes, well, I am,
It's nice to be rid of Father, Mother and the young man

There's just one thing causes me a twinge of pain,
If I take my hat off, shall I find myself home again?
So in this early morning land I always wear my hat
Go home, you see, well I wouldn't run a risk like that.

Stevie Smith

Functional Skills Maths

If there are 4.5 litres in a gallon and
Gary's car does 52 miles to the gallon and
there's a petrol station 5 kilometres away,
where petrol is 2p per litre cheaper,
is it worth Gary making the extra journey?

When Gary pulls onto the ring-road
he senses a darker side,
beyond the edge of sodium town.
He knows the woods are waiting for him,
flicking stars between their fingertips.
He perks in a lay-by, leaves the car,
eyes wide to the deep, black heart of the wood,
and just like in a fairy tale,
he is never seen again.

You must show your workings, you must
explain assumptions used.
Values must be clearly stated.

Helen Cadbury

The Burning

It was the hard winter she came,
frozen larks plummeting through the gloom like falling stars,
each pail in the yard a slattern's looking glass.

Each dusk, the house cobwebbed by creeping frost,
my husband slipped like a knife from an oyster,
my sons nestled like dormice in their cots,
I stood at my black window and oh
the cold it pressed upon me like a lover,
held its hands to my throat, my knees.

She came first through the trees:
a small glint amongst the poplars,
hoarfrost dripping from the velvet nubs of their antlers,
leaping fast to a shuddering pillar of flame,
her pelvis a cradle of jeweled tinder,
her ribs white kindling. A holy thing—
such furious unblossoming—and something profane.

I pressed my eye to the glass, the crackling dark,
saw her heart catch light,
blackbirds flap frantic from the forks of trees—
  —woke shivering, sweat between my breasts,
my tongue in my teeth.

Every night then she came
in the stolen hours between caring and dream,
the children vanished, the drudging chaos of day
put to sleep.
I have no words to tell of the shapes she scorched,
the frozen lock, the copper key,
but that heat licked me raw as a wild love,
cracked the ice on my ribs and tossed in a flare.

All my life I have been a good woman,
compliant, neat, my children's snow boots polished,
each snowflake of ash swept clean from my step.
I've worn obedience like a uniform,
the hoof of the iron cooling in my grate.
Yet I riled in the witching hour, tongue glittering.
My darling, I whispered to my own dry bones,
for what do you burn?

Three moons she has been absent,
though I wait at my window, the chill persisting, presaging
    snow,
and my longing rises hopeless as the carp in the pool.
I don't know where she is living
or if she lives at all—
with women nursing in fevered sheets
or scrubbing floors until their knuckles ignite?

But by dark, when my sons sail the black cut
of sleep, and frost lays its terrible lace
upon the grass, when I am alone with my fretting,
with my dreams like black pearls in the clam of my mouth,
I press my fists to that tenderest wound—my soul—
and Christ how I burn.

Liz Berry

Laurel in the Berkshires

Sea-foam
And coral! Oh, I'll
Climb the great pasture rocks
And dream me mermaid in the sun's
Gold flood.

Adelaide Crapsey

Iridescent lizard

I've had enough
of chasing my tail
like an iridescent lizard:
frantic, frenzied, foolish,
reeling and slipping
in lunatic vicious circles
while I wait for the sun
to push through the ozone layer.

Fear is a many-planed mirror:
I look at my reflection
and see my face
mutilated
in its crystal waters
and my locks of stray hair waving
like a feathery anemone.

I've had it up to here with
being a person of limitations:
I want to be a chameleon,
a real one, multi-coloured,
with eyelashes like Garbo's
and a curly tail;
or a sea flower
exquisite and sticky
with petally fingers
opening and twining
and wriggling and writhing.

Elin Llwyd Morgan

The Forlorn Sea

Our Princess married
A fairy King,
It was a sensational
Wedding.

Now they live in a palace
Of porphyry,
Far, far away,
By the forlorn sea.

Sometimes people visit them,
Last week they invited me;
That is how I can tell you
They live by a forlorn sea.

(They said: Here's a magic carpet,
Come on this,
And when you arrive
We will give you a big kiss.)

I play in the palace garden,
I climb the sycamore tree,
Sometimes I swim
In the forlorn sea.

The King and the Princess are shadowy,
Yet beautiful,
They are waiting on by white cats,
Who are dutiful.

It is like a dream
When they kiss and cuddle me,
But I like it, I like it,
I do not wish to break free.

So I eat all they give me
Because I have read
If you eat fairy food
You will never wake up in your own bed,

But will go on living,
As has happened to me,
Far, far away
By a forlorn sea.

Stevie Smith

The Celestial Announcer

On the day that you hear
the station announcer
call out the towns and villages
of your life, as if she'd read
the very chapters of your soul,
that knowing way she has of saying *Halifax*,
the way she skirts around poor rainy *Manchester*,
and jumps to the conclusion now of *Luddenden*
– with its ghost of a station
and dream of Branwell drunk under the stars –
and all the big and little places
you have ever been, would like to go,
chanted, charted;
well, then you realise it's time to change
your mind, ticket, journey,
point of departure,
Estimated Time of Arrival
and know that she will lend you wings
for those golden slippers, milk and honey,
bread, roses and a brand new map.

Maura Dooley

The Levitation of St Christina

(reputed by witnesses to have flown like a bird from her coffin during her own requiem mass – Saint-Truiden, Flanders, 1182)

I rise on a wing and a prayer. In the aisles Father Thomas
is singing his heart out O Lamb of God all shaven and shorn
and loud enough to waken the dead. Have mercy upon us.

Up here in the gods where anything goes I am Lucifer, born
like a swan from a box, striking the light and standing well clear
of the tears, of the tar and the feathers, and of the coffin's yawn

that takest away Father Thomas's face, that waning moon in
                                the filthy air,
that gaping wound in the side of the world. And the O in his
                                  mouth
is the sins, is enough to make the angels weep. Receive our
                                  prayer.

Out of the hive of the yet to be born, I'm the queen bee,
behemoth
in the candle's flame, shifting my shape in the smoke dance,
the dance of death, whose sting is the needle fixed on
celestial north.

I leap, and my shadow's a shroud-span over the mountains,
an icy stroke
down the cheek of the earth. I have only to touch the hills
and they shall smoke.

Jane Draycott

Ego Tripping (There May Be a Reason Why)

I was born in the congo
I walked to the fertile crescent and built
    the sphinx
I designed a pyramid so tough that a star
    that only glows every one hundred years falls
    into the center giving divine perfect light
I am bad

I sat on the throne
    drinking nectar with allah
I got hot and sent an ice age to europe
    to cool my thirst
My oldest daughter is nefertiti
    the tears from my birth pains
    created the nile
I am a beautiful woman

I gazed on the forest and burned
    out the sahara desert
    with a packet of goat's meat
    and a change of clothes
I crossed it in two hours
I am a gazelle so swift
    so swift you can't catch me

For a birthday present when he was three
I gave my son hannibal an elephant
He gave me rome for mother's day
My strength flows ever on

My son noah built new/ark and
I stood proudly at the helm
   as we sailed on a soft summer day
I turned myself into myself and was
  jesus
   men intone my loving name
   All praises All praises
I am the one who would save

I sowed diamonds in my back yard
My bowels deliver uranium
   the filings from my fingernails are
   semi-precious jewels
   On a trip north
I caught a cold and blew
My nose giving oil to the arab world
I am so hip even my errors are correct
I sailed west to reach east and had to round off
   the earth as I went
   The hair from my head thinned and gold was laid
   across three continents

I am so perfect so divine so ethereal so surreal
I cannot be comprehended
   except by my permission

I mean . . . I . . . can fly
   like a bird in the sky . . .

Nikki Giovanni

'Silence and a space of sleep': Travels towards Tranquillity

These verses celebrate or yearn for quiet times: in one, a hot Venetian afternoon; in another, the sun rising slowly over a southern sea. Each of the poets dreams of rest and relaxation and their words are a shortcut to that feeling for the reader, too, as we imagine gliding away across a quiet loch or sinking gratefully beneath the crust of a mountain.

It feels right, somehow, to close this volume with peaceful poems. Before we locked down, we lived our lives at a pace that would have seemed alarmingly frenetic to any previous generation, with snatched moments of tranquillity being precious and few. It remains to be seen whether we can carry any new, quiet pleasures from this strange time back into the reopened world when it comes. Life, even when we're witnessing it mediated by screens in our own homes, can be loud. As well as a magic carpet, poetry can be an antidote. Reach for it whenever you need to.

from Verses Written in the Chiosk of the British Palace at Pera

Yet not these prospects, all profusely gay –
The gilded navy that adorns the sea,
The rising city in confusion fair,
Magnificently formed, irregular,
Where woods and palaces at once surprise,
Gardens on gardens, domes on domes arise,
And endless beauties tire the wandering eyes –
So soothes my wishes, or so charms my mind,
As this retreat, secure from humankind.
No knave's successful craft does spleen excite,
No coxcomb's tawdry splendour shocks my sight,
No mob-alarm awakes my female fears,
No unrewarded merit asks my tears,
Nor praise my mind, nor envy hurts my ear,
Even fame itself can hardly reach me here;
Impertinence, with all her tattling train,
Fair-sounding flattery's delicious bane;
Censorious folly, noisy party rage,
The thousand tongues with which she must engage,
Who dare have virtue in a vicious age.

Lady Mary Wortley Montagu

Southern Sunrise

Color of lemon, mango, peach,
These storybook villas
Still dream behind
Shutters, their balconies
Fine as hand-
Made lace, or a leaf-and-flower pen-sketch.

Tilting with the winds,
On arrowy stems,
Pineapple-barked,
A green crescent of palms
Sends up its forked
Firework of fronds.

A quartz-clear dawn
Inch by bright inch
Gilds all our Avenue,
And out of the blue drench
Of Angels' Bay
Rises the round red watermelon sun.

Sylvia Plath

Lochan

(for Jean Johnstone)

When all this is over I mean
to travel north, by the high

drove roads and cart tracks
probably in June,

with the gentle dog-roses
flourishing beside me. I mean

to find among the thousands
scattered in that land

a certain quiet lochan,
where water lilies rise

like small fat moons,
and tied among the reeds,

underneath a rowan,
a white boat waits.

Kathleen Jamie

Birthday Poem from Venice

From this swaying city,
Luck. Red peppers bob in the canal,
Red ribbons on hats.

Holy gold is splashed
Everywhere, as if the first Wise Man
Had torn his moneybags.

Everyone fits in here,
Feels at home. One very hot afternoon
A ghost yawned.

We come across
Two slight acquaintances from NW3
Nuzzling at a Bellini.

Gimmicks as usual.
This year it is illuminated yo-yos,
A square full of fireflies.

Through the centuries
Untold valuable things have fallen
Into the water.

A column lies there idle
And leaves a gap-toothed church. One relic
A saint dived for,

Brought back to the shore
To everyone's amazement, doing breast stroke
With steady halo.

Today is paradisal.
A cat, five minutes created, sits with a pigeon.
Happy birthday.

Patricia Beer

'Leave Krete'

Leave Krete and come to this holy temple
where the graceful grove of apple trees
circles an altar smoking with frankincense.

Here roses leave shadows on the ground
and cold springs babble through apple branches
where shuddering leaves pour down profound sleep.

In our meadow where horses graze
and wild flowers of spring blossom,
anise shoots fill the air with aroma.

And here, Aphrodite, pour
heavenly nectar into gold cups
and fill them gracefully with sudden joy.

Sappho

Dzoka (Return)

In the day,
hike this mountain
to find that place
to call home

where you can lay
your tired bones
& spread them
under the sun.

When it sets —
swallow up these nights.
With their clusters of stars,

swallow up these nights
that remind you of home
and its inky nights
around fires

　　and the moon
as a woman,
with the small child on her back,
　　　singing . . .

Dzoka haungafe
    Dzoka haungatye
       Kufa haungafe
Kutya haungatye
           Dzoka
   Kufa kutya
Dzoka, dzoka-a, dzoka
haungafe,
     dzoka haungatye.
Kufa   kutya — dzoka-a

In the day, hike this mountain
to find that place to call home
where you can lay your tired bones
& spread them under
       the sun

       Belinda Zhawi

The Girl Who Fell in Love With the Mountain

I kissed the southern face of a mountain;

his coat scrubbed coarse; smelt of bones
and the iron blood from ruined stone.
The earth moved with me, fell beneath my lips
and I was received into earnest mud;
an ancient epidermis of soft heathers, grass,
and gallant crags enclosing me as his hill-bairn.
I lay immersed, fingering vast feathers
tickling to tender licks, his form; my body-palm
and all the while I rested there
the sunlight streaked my hair with white.

Caroline Hardaker

Translation

We trekked into a far country,
My friend and I.
Our deeper content was never spoken,
But each knew all the other said.
He told me how calm his soul was laid
By the lack of anvil and strife.
'The working kestrel,' I said, 'mutes his mating-note
To please the harmony of this sweet silence.'
And when at the day's end
We laid tired bodies 'gainst
The loose warm sands,
And the air fleeced its particles for a coverlet;
When star after star came out
To guard their lovers in oblivion —
My soul so leapt that my evening prayer
Stole my morning song!

Anne Spencer

Furness Abbey

I wish for the days of the olden time,
When the hours were told by the abbey chime,
When the glorious stars looked down through the midnight
   dim,
Like approving saints on the choir's sweet hymn:
I think of the days we are living now,
And I sigh for those of the veil and the vow.

I would be content alone to dwell
Where the ivy shut out the sun from my cell,
With the death's-head at my side, and the missal on my knee,
Praying to that heaven which was opening to me:
Fevered and vain are the days I lead now,
And I sigh for those of the veil and the vow.

Silken broidery no more would I wear,
Nor golden combs in my golden hair;
I wore them but for one, and in vain they were worn;
My robe should be of serge, my crown of the thorn:
'Tis a cold false world we dwell in now,
And I sigh for the days of the veil and the vow.

I would that the cloister's quiet were mine;
In the silent depths of some holy shrine.
I would tell my blessed beads, and would weep away
From my inmost soul every stain of clay:
My heart's young hopes they have left me now,
And I sigh for the days of the veil and the vow.

Letitia Elizabeth Landon

Not for that City

Not for that city of the level sun,
  Its golden streets and glittering gates ablaze –
  The shadeless, sleepless city of white days,
White nights, or nights and days that are as one –
We weary, when all said, all thought, all done,
  We strain our eyes beyond this dusk to see
  What, from the threshold of eternity
We shall step into. No, I think we shun
The splendour of that everlasting glare,
  The clamour of that never-ending song.
  And if for anything we greatly long,
It is for some remote and quiet stair
  Which winds to silence and a space of sleep
  Too sound for waking and for dreams too deep.

Charlotte Mew

About the Poets

Fleur Adcock (born 1934)

Fleur moved from her native New Zealand to England during the Second World War, returning to settle in London in 1963. She has been writing since she was five, working as a librarian before becoming a full-time writer. Fleur has published ten poetry collections as well as a collected edition, and often gives voice to the powerless in her work. She was awarded an OBE in 1996 and the Queen's Gold Medal for Poetry in 2006.

Londoner is on page 24.

Effie Afton (1829–1887)

Effie's real name was Sarah Elizabeth Harper Monmouth. She also wrote sensational stories under the name Kate Caper and prim Sunday School stories as Sophia Homespun. Entrusted with the decoration of a local New Hampshire church to raise charitable funds, Sarah went the extra mile and embroidered elaborate trappings over a period of years. She gave dramatic tours of the famous 'Worsted Church', which was even featured in the *New York Times*. Having lost her fortune in an unwise investment, Sarah published a frugal 1880 memoir, *Living on Half a Dime a Day* – though she always reserved some of her meagre income for books.

untitled poem – on travel is on page 6.

Gillian Allnutt (born 1949)

Gillian has published nine collections of poetry. *Nantucket and the Angel* and *Lintel* were both shortlisted for the T. S. Eliot Prize, she won the Northern Rock Foundation Writer's Award in 2005 and she received a Cholmondeley Award in 2010. Her retrospective *How the Bicycle Shone* (2007) was a Poetry Book Society Special Commendation. Since 1983 she has taught creative writing in universities, schools and adult education centres. Gillian held a Royal Literary Fund Fellowship at Newcastle and Leeds Universities (2001–2003) and held a writing residency with Freedom From Torture, working with asylum seekers (2009–2010). She received The Queen's Gold Medal for Poetry in 2017. A photograph of Gillian is on display at the National Portrait Gallery. *Ode* is on page 64.

Ruth Awolola (born 1998)

Ruth is a British born Nigerian Jamaican student, youth worker, sister, daughter, friend and poet. She has been performing poetry since 2015 and has performed up and down the UK, exploring themes of travelling, race, family and space. In 2018 *Rising Stars*, an anthology of poetry from new poets, including Ruth, was Highly Commended at the CLiPPA ceremony. Ruth is training to be a full-time educator. *Wolves* is on page 63.

Anna Letitia Barbauld (1743–1825)

Anna badgered her father to teach her languages, the classics and other things not considered necessary for a woman's education — much to her mother's consternation, as she thought her bookishness would put off potential husbands. She was wrong — Anna had offers from several men, including, it is thought, French revolutionary Jean-Paul Marat. The man she chose was, tragically, deeply disturbed and became violent, once chasing her round the kitchen with a knife until she leapt out of the window. He was institutionalized, but escaped and was discovered drowned, and Anna was distraught. Her glittering literary career saw her hobnobbing with the foremost writers of her day, producing poems, political essays, criticism and children's literature dedicated to her nephew, Charles, whom she had adopted as her own. Praised as one of the nation's greatest writers during her lifetime, her reputation suffered in the following centuries and she was remembered – if at all – as a children's writer until rediscovered by feminist scholars in the late twentieth century.

Extract from *Washing Day* is on page 90.

Patricia Beer (1919–1999)

Patricia was born into the strict Plymouth Brethren sect in Devon. Her mother died when Patricia was fourteen and this – perhaps combined with the fact that one grandfather made tombstones and the other coffins – might have inspired her often darkly witty writing about death. She was deliberately vague about her date of birth, which was usually incorrectly given when her work was anthologized. Patricia studied in Exeter and then at Oxford, and taught in Italy and London before returning to Devon. She wrote a historical novel set there, and a memoir of her childhood.

Birthday Poem from Venice is on page 209.

Greta Bellamacina (born 1990)

Greta is a poet, actress and filmmaker. Born in London, she studied at RADA and King's College London. She wrote and directed the film *Hurt by Paradise*, which was nominated for Best UK Features Film at the Raindance festival. Her 2016 documentary *The Safe House: A Decline of Ideas* campaigned for the preservation of public libraries, and she has edited anthologies and published several poetry collections, the latest being *Tomorrow's Woman* (2020). Greta was shortlisted for Young Poet Laureate of London in 2014 and in 2019 her first bilingual collection, translated by Juan

José Vélez Otero, was published in Spanish.
New Glass is on page 118.

Fiona Benson (born 1978)

Fiona's work has been shortlisted for the T. S. Eliot Prize in 2015 and 2019. *Vertigo and Ghost* – which includes poems about motherhood and a rapacious Zeus – won Forward Prizes for best collection and best single poem. She was also the recipient of an Eric Gregory Award in 2006. Fiona lives in Devon with her husband and daughters.
Wood Song is on page 127.

Liz Berry (born 1980)

Liz was born in the Black Country and now lives in Birmingham. Her first book of poems, *Black Country*, was a Poetry Book Society Recommendation, received a Somerset Maugham Award and won the Geoffrey Faber Memorial Award and Forward Prize for Best First Collection 2014. Her pamphlet *The Republic of Motherhood* was a Poetry Book Society choice and the title poem won the Forward Prize for Best Single Poem 2018. Liz is a patron of Writing West Midlands and tutors for organizations, including the Arvon Foundation and The Poetry School.
The Burning is on page 191.

Caroline Bird (born 1986)

Born in Leeds, Caroline has published six collections of poetry and had several of her plays performed at venues including the Lyric Theatre, Hammersmith, and the Southbank Centre. She has been shortlisted for the T. S. Eliot Award, the Ted Hughes Award and twice for the Dylan Thomas Prize. She has won an Eric Gregory Award (2002) and the Foyle Young Poet of the Year award two years running (1999, 2000).

Caroline's poems have been widely published and broadcast, and she was one of five official poets at the 2012 London Olympics. She performs at festivals, leads school workshops and regularly teaches at the Arvon Foundation, as well as being a writer-in-residence for the charity First Story.

Megan Married Herself is on page 29.

Eavan Boland (1944–2020)

Eavan published her first poetry while studying at Trinity College, Dublin, and subsequently published many collections of poetry and essays, edited several anthologies and won numerous awards and plaudits. Her work has been quoted on notable occasions by former Irish Taoiseach Bertie Ahern and Barack Obama. Eavan was inducted into the American Academy of Arts and Sciences in 2016, and in 2018 she was elected to the Royal Irish Academy.

The Pomegranate is on page 36.

Anna Hempstead Branch (1875–1937)

Anna was christened 'the Browning of American poetry' by journalist William Thomas Stead and enjoyed great success during her lifetime. She was born in Connecticut into a distinguished family – her father was a lawyer and her mother a children's author and poet. Her work was strongly influenced by the Victorian Pre-Raphaelite writers, particularly Christina Rossetti. Anna worked with the Christodora House in New York, which supported poverty-stricken and migrant residents. She founded the Poets' Guild whose members – Sara Teasdale and Robert Frost among them – taught residents. Anna was the Vice President of the National League for Women's Service during the First World War.

Sonnet XXV from *Sonnets from a Lock Box* is on page 103.

Anne Brontë (1820–1849)

Anne's novel *Agnes Grey* was inspired by her time as a governess. Its heroine was a petted and patronized youngest sibling who grew up among rugged hills – so we can draw our own conclusions about Brontë family dynamics from that! She had to leave her post after persuading her employers to hire her feckless brother Branwell, who embarked on an affair with the lady of the house. She and her elder sisters Charlotte and Emily published their poetry under male pseudonyms as Acton, Currer and Ellis Bell. Disappointed by pitiful sales of two copies in a year, they worked intensively on their novels instead, pacing the dining room and critiquing each other's work. Anne's novel *The Tenant of Wildfell Hall* – in which a woman flees her cruel, alcoholic husband – was considered shocking but was a huge hit. Anne died from tuberculosis aged only twenty-nine.

Lines Composed in a Wood on a Windy Day is on page 23.

Emily Brontë (1818–1848)

Many of Emily's poems originated in her gothic-flavoured writings about Gondal, an imaginary island realm created with her sister, Anne. Emily's masterpiece *Wuthering Heights* was, like much of her poetry, inspired by the wild beauty of the Yorkshire moors where the sisters lived with their father and brother. She died from tuberculosis aged only thirty.

'*Riches I hold in light esteem*' is on page 129.

Elizabeth Barrett Browning (1806–1861)

Elizabeth received an excellent education at home from her adoring but overprotective father, and published poetry from her teens onwards. Despite living as an invalid and recluse – perhaps devastated at her brother drowning, perhaps injured in a fall from a horse – her poetry was hugely popular. She attracted fan mail from Robert Browning – then an aspiring poet, six years her junior – and their relationship revived her sufficiently to elope with him to Italy, get married and have a son. Her father never forgave them. A greater celebrity than her husband during their lifetimes, Elizabeth also involved herself in contemporary politics. She was a passionate critic of slavery and child labour, and her epic poem *Aurora Leigh* was remarkable for its strong heroine and contemporary setting.

Extract from *Aurora Leigh* is on page 74.

Colette Bryce (born 1970)

Colette is an award-winning poet from Northern Ireland. Born and brought up in Derry, she moved to England as a student in 1988 and settled in London for some years before starting out as a writer. She received the Eric Gregory Award for emerging poets in 1995. After a year teaching in Madrid, she took up a fellowship at Dundee University from 2002 to 2005, and was subsequently appointed North East Literary Fellow at the Universities of Newcastle and Durham. She currently lives in Newcastle-upon-Tyne where she works as a freelance writer and editor.

The Full Indian Rope Trick is on page 104.

Helen Burke (born 1953)

Helen was born in Doncaster to Irish parents and started writing poetry in 1989. Her poems have been widely published and anthologized, and she has won numerous prizes. Since the 1970s, Helen's poems have appeared in pamphlets, on greetings cards, on pieces of origami, on radio, on tape, on CD, on the side of stray dogs and in a million other places. Her verses have been set to music by an Australian orchestra and she has performed with jazz, rock and Irish folk musicians. *The Road Out of Town* is on page 59.

Helen Cadbury (1965–2017)

Helen was a British crime fiction author, poet and playwright, whose debut novel *To Catch a Rabbit* won the Northern Crime Award. Born in the Midlands, Helen grew up near Oldham and spent the last 15 years of her life in York. When she was a child she wanted to be an actor, a writer, or an ice cream man's assistant – and achieved the first two ambitions. The first collection of her poetry, *Forever, Now*, was published in November 2017.
Functional Skills Maths is on page 190.

Jen Campbell (born 1987)

Jen is an award-winning poet, children's author and short story writer. She has received an Eric Gregory Award and won the Jane Martin Poetry Prize. Jen worked as a bookseller for ten years and wrote the *Sunday Times* bestselling *Weird Things Customers Say in Bookshops* series. She appears regularly on BBC Radio 5 Live, is Vlogger in Residence for the Poetry Book Society, has a popular YouTube channel and a podcast, runs online working workshops and speaks at schools, universities and book festivals.
December is on page 117.

Moya Cannon (born 1965)

Moya was born in County Donegal and now lives in Dublin. She has taught in various schools and universities, been writer in residence at Trent University Ontario and Kerry County Council, and edited *Poetry Ireland* in 1995. Moya has collaborated with musicians including traditional Irish singers and a string quartet, and a bilingual Spanish/

English edition of her poems was published in Spain in 2015, translated by respected Argentinian poet Jorge Fondebrider.

Driving Back Over the Blue Ridge / Hunter's Moon are on pages 68 and 152.

J. R. Carpenter (born 1972)

J. R. Carpenter is a Canadian-born UK-based artist, writer and practice-led researcher working across print, performance and digital media. Her web-based work *The Gathering Cloud* won the New Media Writing Prize 2016, and her debut novel *Words the Dog Knows* won the Expozine Alternative Press Award for Best English Book. Her poetry collection *An Ocean of Static* was highly commended by the Forward Prizes 2018.

Extract from *Notes on the Voyage of Owl and Girl* is on page 165.

Mary Jean Chan (born 1990)

Mary is the author of *Flèche*, a 2019 Poetry Book Society Recommendation and the winner of the 2019 Costa Book Award for Poetry. The title poem from her debut collection won the 2018 Poetry Society Geoffrey Dearmer Prize, and she is the recipient of a 2019 Eric Gregory Award for her pamphlet *A Hurry of English*. Born and raised in Hong Kong, Mary is Lecturer in Creative Writing (Poetry) at Oxford Brookes University and lives in London.

The Window is on page 39.

Jennifer Chang

Jennifer was born in New Jersey and studied for a PhD at the University of Virginia. Her poems have been published in publications including *The New Yorker*, *Poetry* and *The Nation*. She has published the collections *The History of Anonymity* (2008) and *Some Say the Lark* (2017), the latter winning the 2018 William Carlos Williams Award. Jennifer lives with her family in Washington D. C. and is Assistant Professor of English and Creative Writing at George Washington University. She co-chairs the Advisory Board of Kundiman, an organization that supports and promotes Asian American literature.

Obedience, or The Lying Tale is on page 40.

Kate Clanchy (born 1965)

Kate was born and grew up in Scotland but now lives in Oxford. Her poetry collections *Slattern*, *Samarkand* and *Newborn* have brought her many literary awards and a wide audience. She is the author of *Antigona and Me*, and was the 2009 winner of the BBC Short Story Award. She has also written extensively for Radio 4. Her first novel, *Meeting the English*, was shortlisted for the 2013 Costa First Book Award. Kate's anthology of poems from the students of Oxford Spires Academy, *England: Poems from a School*, was published in 2018, and her acclaimed memoir of her life in education, *Some Kids I Taught and What They Taught Me*, in 2019. In 2018, she was awarded an MBE for Services to Literature.

Dare is on page 160.

Polly Clark (born 1968)

Polly Clark has had various jobs, including zoo-keeping and teaching English in Hungary. Her poetry has won many prizes, including the Eric Gregory Award, and she was selected as one of *Mslexia* magazine's ten best poets of the decade in 2014. Her novels *Larchfield* (2017) and *Tiger* (2019), which was shortlisted for the Saltire Scottish Novel of the Year 2019, have attracted widespread critical acclaim. Polly divides her time between Scotland and a London house boat.

Hedgehog is on page 35.

Gillian Clarke (born 1937)

Gillian was born in Cardiff to Welsh-speaking parents, though she grew up speaking English and only later learned Welsh herself. She has written many poetry collections for adults and children, as well as plays for theatre and radio. She translates poetry and prose from Welsh, and her own work has been translated into ten languages. Gillian was the National Poet of Wales from 2008 to 2016. Her prize-winning poems are studied on the GCSE and A-Level syllabus, and she performs regularly for Poetry Live!

In a Cardiff Arcade, 1952 is on page 72.

Mary Elizabeth Coleridge (1861–1907)

Mary was the great-great-niece of Romantic poet Samuel Taylor Coleridge, but was better known during her life for her eerie, imaginative novels. She was too shy to publish her poetry under the famous family name, so she did so under the pseudonym 'Anodos'. Her poetry only reached a wide audience after her death when another poet, Henry Newbolt, published them under her real name. Mary never married and devoted most of her time to lecturing at the Working Women's College in London.

I Had a Boat is on page 134

Charly Cox

Charly is a writer, producer and poet. Her writing focuses on destigmatizing mental health and the coming-of-age of a young woman surviving the modern world. In January 2017, she published her first poem on Instagram, showing her internet followers her poetry for the first time. Named one of the 20 power players to watch out for in 2018 by *Elle* magazine, Charly has published two books: *She Must Be Mad* (2018) and *Validate Me* (2019).

kids is on page 42.

Adelaide Crapsey (1878–1914)

Adelaide was born in Brooklyn Heights, New York. She studied archaeology in Rome and taught history, literature and poetry. Having concealed her poor health from her family as long as she could, she eventually died of tuberculosis in 1914. Two books, a poetry collection entitled *Verse* and a study on *English Metrics*, were published after her death. Although she wrote fewer than a hundred poems, she wrote right up until her death in hospital – often, understandably, on the theme of dying. Inspired in part by Japanese three-line haiku poems, Adelaide invented the cinquain, a poetic form with five lines.

Release / Laurel in the Berkshires are on pages 120 and 194.

Sarah Crossan (born 1981)

Sarah holds degrees in Creative Writing and Philosophy and Literature, and trained as an English and drama teacher. Her novels *Apple and Rain* and *The Weight of Water* were both shortlisted for the Carnegie Medal, and *One* (2015) was awarded the Carnegie Medal along with *The Bookseller* Prize for Young Adult fiction, the CLiPPA Poetry Award and the Irish Children's Book of the Year. In 2018, she was appointed Laureate na nÓg, or Irish Children's laureate. Sarah often speaks in schools promoting reading and creative writing.

In Wellies is on page 22.

Emily Wilding Davison (1872–1913)

Emily was one of the most active and militant of the suffragettes. When peaceful campaigning had no effect, she turned to fierce action to fight for women's votes, from smashing windows and setting fire to post boxes to hiding overnight in the Houses of Parliament. She was imprisoned on numerous occasions. Her motive for running on to the racetrack during the Epsom Derby in June 1913 is unknown. She may have meant to attach a suffragette flag to one of the horses, but King George V's horse trampled her and she later died of her injuries. Her coffin was accompanied by battalions of suffragettes and their supporters at every stage of its journey from Epsom to her final resting place of Newcastle. 'L'Envoi' was published in *Holloway Jingles*, a collection of verses written by suffragettes incarcerated in Holloway prison in 1912, smuggled out and published by the Glasgow branch of the Women's Social and Political Union.

L'Envoi is on page 116.

Jan Dean (born 1950)

Jan runs workshops in schools, libraries and even cathedrals, encouraging people to write. She has published children's fiction and poetry collections, including the CLiPPA shortlisted *Wallpapering the Cat*. She says, 'Writing poems is wonderfully strange – like playing lucky dip with a barrelful of tigers, raspberry jellies and machine parts.'

Miss Aylward's Journey is on page 111.

Emily Dickinson (1830–1886)

Emily was from an upper-crust Massachusetts family and was apparently a sociable girl until something – scholars are divided about whether this might have been an unrequited love affair, or mental health struggles – led her to withdraw from the world. She retreated into the house, dressed all in white, and wrote almost 2,000 passionate poems which were discovered after her death. Some were neatly bound in little books, while others were scribbled on envelopes and the recipes she loved to cook. Only a handful were published before Emily's death, and early editions 'corrected' her unusual punctuation. It wasn't until 1955 that they appeared in print as she had written them, but she is now acknowledged to be one of history's most important and best-loved poets.

Not knowing when the Dawn will come / Exultation is the Going are on pages 11 and 164.

Maura Dooley (born 1957)

Maura is a poet and freelance writer. Her collections *Explaining Magnetism* (1991), *Kissing A Bone* (1996) and *The Silvering* (2016) were Poetry Book Society recommendations. *Life Under Water* (2008) and *Kissing a Bone* were shortlisted for the T. S. Eliot Prize. Maura has also edited poetry anthologies and essay collections. She was a Centre Director at the Arvon Foundation and founded the Southbank Centre's Literature programme. Maura has been a judge for the T. S. Eliot Prize and the National Poetry Competition, and has chaired the Poetry Book Society. She is now based in London, and is Reader in Creative Writing at Goldsmiths College, University of London.

The Celestial Announcer is on page 199.

Jane Draycott (born 1954)

Jane is a poet and translator who has been nominated three times for the Forward Prize for Poetry, and several of her collections have been Poetry Book Society Recommendations. Her collection *Over* was shortlisted for the 2009 T. S. Eliot Prize. Jane was named as one of the Poetry Book Society's Next Generation poets in 2004 and won the 2014 Hippocrates International Prize for Poetry and Medicine. Her audio, film and collaborative work has won awards, including BBC Radio 3 Poem-for-Radio, and she has been poet-in-residence in Amsterdam and at the River & Rowing Museum in Henley, Oxfordshire. Jane teaches at Oxford University and the University of Lancaster.

The Levitation of St Christina is on page 200.

Carol Ann Duffy (born 1955)

Carol Ann was born in Glasgow. She grew up in Stafford and then attended the University of Liverpool, where she studied Philosophy. She has written for both children and adults, and her poetry has received many awards, including the Signal Prize for Children's Verse, the Whitbread and Forward Prizes, as well as the Lannan Award and the E. M. Forster Prize in America. She was Poet Laureate 2009–2019, and in 2012 she was awarded the PEN Pinter Prize.

Away and See / In Your Mind is on page are on pages 14 and 178.

Sasha Dugdale (born 1974)

Sasha is a poet, playwright and translator. From 1995 to 2000, she worked for the British Council in Russia, and she translates Russian poetry and drama. She is the author of poetry collections *Notebook* (2003), *The Estate* (2007), *Red House* (2011) and *Joy* (2017), and has won the Forward Poetry Prize for Best Single Poem and the Cholmondeley Award. Sasha edited *Modern Poetry in Translation* from 2012 to 2017, and is currently poet-in-residence at St John's College, Cambridge, and co-director of the Winchester Poetry Festival.

* is on page 53.

Sarah Egerton (1668–1723)

As a teenager, Sarah published 'The Female Advocate' (1686), a stinging riposte to 'Love Given O'er' (1682) by Robert Gould which attacked the 'pride, lust and inconstancy' of women. Her horrified father banished her from London for this transgression, packing her off to relatives in the country. She was widowed young, and her second marriage – to a second cousin twenty years her senior, rather than Henry Pierce to whom many of her poems are dedicated – was scandalously stormy. The author Delarivier Manley attacked Sarah's looks, called her a 'She-Devil incarnate' and claimed 'she's in love with all the handsome Fellows she sees' – though it's worth noting that she was far from unbiased since they had quarrelled viciously. Despite furious legal battles Sarah and her unhappy husband were not granted a divorce. Her work often raged passionately against women being denied freedom and education.

Extract from *The Emulation* is on page 78.

Safia Elhillo (born 1990)

Safia is the author of *The January Children* (winner of the 2016 Sillerman First Book Prize for African Poets). Sudanese by way of Washington, DC, she holds an MFA from The New School, a Cave Canem Fellowship and a Fellowship from the Poetry Foundation, and was listed in Forbes Africa's 2018 '30 Under 30'. Safia is a Pushcart Prize nominee and co-winner of the 2015 Brunel International African Poetry Prize. Her work has been translated into several languages and she is co-editor of the anthology *Halal If You Hear Me*.

border/softer is on page 5.

Rebecca Elson (1960–1999)

A distinguished Canadian-American astronomer, Rebecca was one of the world's leading researchers into star clusters and galaxy formation. She also climbed mountains on three continents, spoke three languages, played the mandolin, cooked wonderfully and was a star striker in her Saturday League football team. Rebecca was diagnosed with non-Hodgkin's lymphoma at the age of twenty-nine and died tragically young, aged only thirty-nine.

The Hubble Space Telescope before repair is on page 147.

Laura Fairgrieve

Laura received her MFA from Adelphi University, New York, where she currently teaches writing. She is a recipient of the 2016 Poets & Writers Amy Award. Her work has appeared in publications including *Mortar Magazine*, *East Coast Ink* and *Underwater New York*. She lives in Brooklyn.

Sally Ride Speaks to the Schoolgirls is on page 139.

Eleanor Farjeon (1881–1965)

Eleanor grew up in London. She was a quiet, bookish child. Although she had little formal education, the household was full of artists and writers and her father encouraged her writing endeavours from earliest childhood. She became best known as a writer of poetry and stories for children, and counted many famous writers, including D. H. Lawrence and Edward Thomas, about whom she wrote a book, among her friends. Eleanor was the author of the hymn 'Morning has Broken'.

The Distance is on page 2.

Nikita Gill (born 1987)

Nikita was born in Belfast but grew up in New Delhi, where an inspiring teacher encouraged her to publish a short story about her grandfather in a newspaper. She has gained an enormous online following, and her first collection *Wild Embers* was published in 2017. *Fierce Fairytales* (2018) and *Great Goddesses* (2019) followed, in which Nikita writes and illustrates feminist reimaginings of traditional tales and classical myths, and she also edited *Slam! You're Gonna Wanna Hear This*, a collection of performance poetry (2020).

Persephone to Demeter is on page 38.

Beatrice R. Gibbs

Born in Devon and educated at Sherborne School for Girls in Dorset, Beatrice became Co-Principal of Somerville School in Sussex. She was a poet and journalist and also wrote short fiction and children's books. *The Bomber* is on page 99.

Charlotte Perkins Gilman (1860–1935)

Charlotte's father abandoned his family and she grew up in poverty, receiving little formal education, in Connecticut. She had relationships with women and men throughout her life and was married twice. The bout of depression Charlotte suffered after the birth of her daughter inspired her most famous work, the short story *The Yellow Wallpaper*, about a woman who is confined to her room by her husband. Charlotte was a vocal campaigner for women's votes and rights and often wrote and lectured about the need to free women from domestic drudgery. *Locked Inside* is on page 115.

Nikki Giovanni (born 1943)

Nikki is an award-winning writer and activist. Initially unable to find a publisher for her work, she self-published. In the 1970s she co-founded a publishing house to promote work by other African-American women. Among numerous other honours, she has now been awarded seven NAACP Awards, nominated for a Grammy, selected as one of Oprah Winfrey's twenty-five 'Living Legends' and been a finalist for the National Book Award. Three of her poetry collections have been *New York Times* bestsellers and she is now a University Distinguished Professor at Virginia Tech. Nikki says, 'I recommend old age; it's fun.' *Ego Tripping (There May Be A Reason Why)* is on page 202.

Diane Glancy (born 1941)

Diane has Cherokee, English and German heritage and was born in Missouri. She writes across several genres, including fiction, non-fiction, poetry and drama, and her work has won awards including the Oklahoma Book Award, the Cherokee Medal of Honor and the Pablo Neruda Prize for Poetry. She has served as artist-in-residence for the Oklahoma State Arts Council and has taught Native American literature and Creative Writing at Macalester College, Minnesota.

Kemo Sabe is on page 82.

Salena Godden (born 1972)

Salena Godden is a poet, activist, broadcaster, essayist and memoirist based in London. She has published several volumes of poetry including *Fishing in the Aftermath* (2014), *Pessimism is for Lightweights* (2019) and a literary childhood memoir, *Springfield Road* (2014). Her spoken-word album *LIVEwire* was shortlisted for the Ted Hughes Award. Salena's debut novel, *Mrs Death Misses Death*, is forthcoming.

Galway Dreaming is on page 7.

Charlotte L. Forten Grimké (1837–1914)

Charlotte's diaries are some of the earliest we have by a free Black woman in America. A teacher and anti-slavery advocate, she was the first Black teacher to teach white students at a Salem school and also volunteered at a South Carolina school for former slaves and their children. After the American Civil War, she worked for the US government recruiting teachers. Charlotte's poems were published under her maiden name and the pseudonyms Miss C.L.F. and 'Lottie' in abolitionist periodicals.

Poem is on page 76.

Marilyn Hacker (born 1942)

Marilyn is a poet, translator and critic. Born in the Bronx to Jewish immigrant parents, she met the future science-fiction writer Samuel R. Delany at school and, although he is gay, they married and had a daughter. Divorced in 1980, they remain friends and Marilyn identifies as a lesbian. Her poetry and translation has won numerous awards, including the 2001 Audre Lorde Award, and in 2013 she was inducted into the New York Writers Hall of Fame. She divides her time between New York and Paris.

Mythology is on page 19.

Norah Hanson (born 1937)

Norah was born in Hull, Yorkshire, and has been a proud resident ever since. She spent her working life teaching in secondary schools, then turned to writing after her retirement in 1996. Widowed in 1994, she is nonetheless not short of company – she has six children, seventeen grandchildren and six great-grandchildren. Her poetry has been shortlisted for the Bridport Prize, featured on BBC Radio 4, and published in numerous magazines and anthologies. She is the author of three collections of poetry, *Love Letters & Children's Drawings* (2011), *Under a Holderness Sky* (2013) and *Sparks* (2016).

She Showed Me Her Dreams is on page 25.

Caroline Hardaker (born 1986)

Caroline's poetry has been published worldwide in magazines and anthologies. Her debut collection, *Bone Ovation*, was published in 2017 and she also writes literary fiction, non-fiction and journalism. Caroline works as a content manager for Newcastle University and is currently working with the Royal Northern College of Music to produce a cycle of operatic art songs.

The Girl Who Fell in Love With the Mountain is on page 214.

Lauren Hollingsworth-Smith

Lauren was a Top 15 winner of the Foyle Young Poets of the Year Award 2019.

I want to stand naked in the school hall is on page 130.

Yü Hsüan-chi (c. 843–868)

We have around fifty poems by this remarkable woman. She was working as a prostitute in Ch'ang An (now Xi'an in Shaanxi Province) until she met Li Yi, to whom many of her poems are addressed. She became his concubine until he abandoned her, upon which she embarked upon a religious life as a Taoist nun. She lived in poverty as the unlikely combination of courtesan, nun and poet until she was executed – on what it is thought were trumped-up charges – for killing her maid.

Staying in the Mountains in Summer is on page 162.

Helen Hunt Jackson (1830–1885)

Helen grew up in Amherst, Massachusetts, and was a lifelong friend of fellow resident Emily Dickinson. She lost her first husband and two young sons and suffered with tuberculosis herself, meeting her second husband while seeking a rest cure in California. Helen took his name, Jackson, in her later writing career although she originally published anonymously under 'H H'. She became an author, poet and activist for the rights of Native Americans, campaigning vigorously on their behalf and publishing both a history and a successful novel (*Ramona*, 1884) that demonstrated their appalling treatment at the hands of the American government.

Emigravit is on page 174.

Kathleen Jamie (born 1962)

As well as poetry, Kathleen has written three non-fiction books: *Findings*, *Sightlines* and *Surfacing.* Her influences and passions include travel, the natural world, art, medicine and archaeology. She reviews for publications including the *Guardian* and has also written for radio. Since 2010, she has held a part-time post as Professor of Poetry at the University of Stirling. A poem of Kathleen's was recently selected by the public to be carved on to the national monument at Bannockburn, Scotland.

Lochan is on page 208.

Georgia Douglas Johnson (1880–1966)

Georgia's parents were of African-American, Native American and English heritage. She was born in Atlanta in her namesake state but moved to New York with her husband and two sons. Her husband didn't encourage her writing but, after his death, her career took off and her home became known as the S Street Salon, a magnet for writers of the Harlem Renaissance, including Anne Spencer and Alice Dunbar-Nelson. She wrote almost thirty plays, including several exposing the evils of racial prejudice, though many remained unpublished during her lifetime due to both her race and her gender. Although she often had to take clerical jobs to support the family, she produced around two hundred poems as well as newspaper columns and over thirty short stories.

Your World is on page 10.

Meena Kandasamy (born 1984)

Meena combines her love for the written word with the struggle for social justice through poetry, translation, fiction and essays. She has published the poetry collections *Touch* (2006) and *Ms Militancy*

(2010) and published novels including the highly acclaimed *When I Hit You: Or, The Portrait of the Writer As A Young Wife* (2017), which was shortlisted for the Women's Prize for Fiction, and *Exquisite Cadavers* (2019). She is also an award-winning translator and non-fiction writer. Meena holds a PhD in sociolinguistics and her work has appeared in eighteen languages. She lives in London.

Sangharsh Karna Hai is on page 113.

Jackie Kay (born 1961)

As well as poetry, Jackie has written plays, children's books and television dramas. She has won awards including the Saltire Society Scottish First Book Award (for *The Adoption Papers*), the Somerset Maugham Award (for *Other Lovers*) and the Guardian Fiction Prize (for *Trumpet*.) Jackie was the third modern Makar (the Scottish Laureate.) She was awarded an MBE in 2006 and is currently Professor of Creative Writing at Newcastle University and Cultural Fellow at Glasgow Caledonian University.

The Moon at Knowle Hill is on page 136.

Anna Kisby

Anna Kisby studied Literature and Film at the Universities of East Anglia, Sussex and Paris-Sorbonne, taught English in Prague and sold cowboy boots in Massachusetts, before training as an archivist and working with women's history collections. Her poems are widely published and her debut pamphlet, *All The Naked Daughters*, appeared in 2017. She won the BBC Proms Poetry competition 2016, the Havant Poetry Competition 2016, and was commended in the Faber New Poets Scheme 2015–2016.

Saint Senara and Me is on page 168.

Vanessa Kisuule

Vanessa has worked with organizations including RADA and the Southbank Centre, and been featured on BBC Radio 4, *The Guilty Feminist* podcast, *Blue Peter*, Sky TV and in the *Guardian* and *Huffington Post*. She has performed at venues including the Royal Albert Hall, the British Library, WOMAD and Glastonbury. She has won more than ten slam titles and represented the UK in two European Slam Championships. Vanessa has published two collections – *Joyriding the Storm* (2014) and *A Recipe for Sorcery* (2017) – and her work was highly commended in the *Forward Prize Anthology* (2019). Her one-woman show SEXY has been on tour, and she is the Bristol City Poet for 2018–2020. In 2020 her poem 'Hollow' about the toppling of a statue of slave-trader Edward Colston went viral.
holiday is on page 97.

Christy Ku

Christy Ku was one of the top six finalists for BBC 1Xtra's Words First programme 2019 and has headlined nights around the UK. She is a Barbican Young Poet alumna and has worked closely with the Barbican Centre on various artistic commissions. Christy is also a short story writer, YouTube journalist, digital content producer, photographer and podcaster, and is working on her debut poetry collection.
'we misread 'language' as 'lavender' is on page 79.

Letitia Elizabeth Landon (1802–1838)

Letitia was better known as L.E.L., the enigmatic initials under which she published poetry in *The Gentleman's Magazine*. They were eagerly awaited by readers, and writers including Elizabeth Barrett Browning and Christina Rossetti composed poems in her praise. She was beset by rumours about a racy love life but eventually married

George Maclean and sailed with him to Ghana – then the Gold Coast – where he was governor. There she died of an overdose of prussic acid which was judged to have been accidental, despite some speculations to the contrary. L.E.L.'s romantic style fell out of fashion after her death, though her work has been rediscovered in recent decades.
The Sea-Shore / Furness Abbey are on pages 155 and 216.

Emma Lazarus (1849–1887)

Emma Lazarus was from a Jewish family in New York. She worked on Ellis Island teaching English to Jews who had fled persecution in Russia, and wrote passionately against anti-Semitism. 'The New Colossus' was written to raise funds to build a pedestal for the Statue of Liberty (the statue itself was a gift to America from France) and it was eventually inscribed upon the monument itself.
The New Colossus is on page 173.

Thyrza Leyshon

Thyrza Leyshon lives and works in Essex. Her poetry has appeared in a range of publications. She also has work included in *Est: Collected reports from East Anglia* and was awarded second prize in Ware Poets competition 2018. Her work was highly commended in *The Forward Book of Poetry 2020*.
Edith Sitwell is on page 124.

Audre Lorde (1934–1992)

Audre was born in New York to West Indian parents and developed a love for poetry at a young age, writing her own verses from her early teens. As well as working as a teacher and librarian, she was an outspoken lifelong activist, writing and fighting against racism, classism and homophobia. Audre was also an important figure in twentieth-century feminism and a pioneering champion of the need for intersectional politics. She had two children in the late 1960s, taught in Berlin during the 1980s and eventually settled with her partner Dr Gloria Joseph in the Caribbean. Having documented her illness in the ground-breaking autobiography *The Cancer Journals*, Audre died of liver cancer at the young age of 58. Just before her death, she took the African name Gamba Adisa, translated as 'Warrior: she who makes her meaning known.'

Coal is on page 87.

Amy Lowell (1874–1925)

Amy was from a prominent Massachusetts family who didn't think their daughters should go to college, but fortunately their mansion had a library stocked with 7,000 books. At twenty-eight she decided to become a poet, so she read intensively for eight years in preparation. She was a poetry pioneer and campaigned forcefully to bring it to a wider audience by lecturing, translating and nurturing new talent. A flamboyant and eccentric figure with a prince-nez, bun, and a cigar permanently in hand, Amy became a poetry celebrity. She lived with actress Ada Dwyer Russell, to whom many of her poems are addressed.

Bath / A Winter Ride / The Crescent Moon / Roads are on pages 27, 67, 138 and 186.

Hollie McNish (born 1983)

Hollie has published the poetry collections *Papers*, *Cherry Pie* and *Plum*, and a poetic memoir of parenthood, *Nobody Told Me*, winner of the Ted Hughes Award for New Work in Poetry 2016. She co-wrote the play *Offside*, which relates the two-hundred year history of UK women's football, and collaborated with the Dutch ensemble, the Metropole Orkest, on her second poetry album *Poetry versus Orchestra*. Hollie tours the UK extensively, and her poetry videos have attracted millions of views worldwide. She has a keen interest in migration studies, infant health and language learning, and gives performances of her work for organizations as diverse as the *Economist*, MTV and Unicef.

Cocoon is on page 61.

Sabrina Mahfouz

Sabrina has recently been elected a Fellow of the Royal Society of Literature and is the recipient of the 2018 King's Alumni Arts & Culture Award. She has won a Sky Arts Academy Award for Poetry, a Westminster Prize for New Playwrights and a Fringe First Award for her play *Chef*. Her play *With a Little Bit of Luck* won the 2019 Best Drama Production at the BBC Radio & Music Awards. She also writes for children and her play *Zeraffa Giraffa* won a 2018 Off West End Award. Sabrina is the editor of *The Things I Would Tell You: British Muslim Women Write* and *Smashing It: Working Class Artists on Life, Art and Making It Happen.* She also contributed an essay to the multi-award-winning *The Good Immigrant*.

Boats in a Storm is on page 171.

Katherine Mansfield (1888–1923)

Born Kathleen Mansfield Beauchamp in Wellington, New Zealand, Katherine is better known as a writer of short stories than as a poet. A passionate and, by all accounts, occasionally difficult character, her love-life was rather complicated: while pregnant with the child of another man, she married her much older music teacher, only to abandon him days later. Rushed away to Germany by her scandalized mother, she suffered a stillbirth. Her relationship with her second husband, John Middleton Murry, was more affectionate by letter than in person. The presence of Ida Baker – the woman she called her 'wife' – was presumably a bone of contention. She died of tuberculosis aged only thirty-four.

Spring Wind in London / Strawberries and the Sailing Ship are on pages 101 and 153.

Charlotte Mew (1869–1928)

Charlotte's middle-class family had little money after her father died, and she and her sister Anne worked to contribute to the household. They had another brother and sister who had been confined to asylums, and Charlotte and Anne vowed never to marry, to avoid passing on mental illness to their children. She wrestled with her faith throughout her life and in her poems, feeling attracted to Roman Catholicism but never actually converting. The deaths of her mother and Anne devastated Charlotte and she sadly took her own life.

Sea Love / Not For That City are on pages 161 and 218.

Edna St Vincent Millay (1892–1950)

Edna enjoyed great success – particularly during the 1920s – and was the third woman to receive the Pulitzer Prize. Raised, often in poverty, by her mother after she left Edna's abusive father, Edna proved herself to be intelligent and determined. After a time at college peppered with love affairs with men and women, she moved to Greenwich Village in New York and had what she later called a 'very, very merry time'. Her direct, feminist poetry was successful and she also wrote lighter, more lucrative, journalism under the name Nancy Boyd. Her later years were marred by illness, but she was still incredibly prolific and produced opera librettos as well as plays, articles and poetry.

Sonnet XXXI is on page 73.

Gabriela Mistral (1889–1957)

Born in a remote village in the Chilean Andes, Gabriela was determined to qualify as a teacher despite being barred from studying because of her political journalism. On succeeding, she taught all around Chile and, later, organized educational programmes in Mexico. Travelling widely, Gabriela spent her life writing and acting in defence of the downtrodden. She worked for the League of Nations in Paris and as a diplomat, always opposing fascism, in Spain and Italy during the turbulent 1930s. In 1945 she was the first Spanish American writer to be awarded the Nobel Prize for Literature.

The Footprint is on page 54.

Elma Mitchell (1919–2000)

Elma was a Scottish poet who worked as a librarian for the BBC. She was fluent in languages including Russian and worked as a translator and freelance writer, publishing poetry from the 1960s onwards. She worked in thatched barn that served as both library and study, and was inhabited by rare bats. Elma read fiercely and brilliantly at her rare public readings, even when she was elderly and frail.

It's the Sea I Want is on page 157.

Lady Mary Wortley Montagu (1689–1762)

Lady Mary's husband was, briefly, the British Ambassador to the Ottoman Empire. Her letters and the verses she wrote in Constantinople – now Istanbul – give a fascinating insight into the city, including the Turkish baths and Sultan's harem, in which the ingenious Mary managed to learn political secrets her husband couldn't access. She pioneered the use of the smallpox vaccination then popular among the Ottomans by volunteering her young children as subjects, though Edward Jenner – who popularized immunization nearly eight years later – gets all the credit in the history books.

Extract from *Verses Written in the Chiosk of the British Palace at Pera* is on page 206.

Virginia Moore (1903–1993)

Virginia published three poetry collections, essays, a novel and historical biographies including studies of women writers. Her most famous book was perhaps *Virginia is a State of Mind* (1942), about her home state's history and geography. Although devoted to, and celebrated in, Virginia, she lectured on literature around America and travelled around the world twice.

Avowal is on page 148.

Elin Llwyd Morgan

Elin is an author and translator at Glyndŵr University, Wrexham. Her debut novel, *Between the Heavens and Las Vegas*, was shortlisted for the Welsh Academy Book of the Year in 2005 and her second novel, *The Moon Has Eyes*, was longlisted for the same prize in 2008. She lives in Wales with her partner and son.

Iridescent lizard is on page 195.

Esther Morgan (born 1970)

Esther was inspired to start writing after volunteering at the Wordsworth Trust, and has published four poetry collections. She has won an Eric Gregory Award, the Bridport Poetry Prize and the Jerwood Aldeburgh First Collection Prize, among other accolades. Esther has taught at the University of East Anglia and in Australia, and now works for the Norfolk Museums Service.

The Long Holidays is on page 21.

About the Poets

Michaela Morgan

Michaela is a children's author and poet who has written more than 140 books. She has visited schools in the UK, Europe, the USA and Africa, and also gives workshops and readings in libraries, at festivals and in prisons. Her latest poetry collections are *Wonderland: Alice in Poetry* and *Reaching the Stars: Poems about Extraordinary Women and Girls* (Macmillan). Michaela is really quite small. But very fierce.

Freedom Poem is on page 20.

Portia Nelson (1920–2001)

Portia was an American singer, songwriter, actress and author. She was a cabaret singer throughout the 1950s, and turned her hand to acting in the 1960s – often, coincidentally, playing nuns, including Sister Berthe in *The Sound of Music*. She wrote hundreds of songs, and was a voice coach for Hollywood stars including Jane Russell. Her book *There's A Hole in My Sidewalk* (1977) became a key text in self-help and addiction recovery.

Autobiography in Five Chapters is on page 57.

Grace Nichols (born 1950)

Grace was born in Guyana, and moved to Britain in 1977. Her first book, *I is a Long-Memoried Woman*, won the Commonwealth Poetry Prize in 1983, and she has also written stories and poems for children and a novel. She is inspired by folklore and Caribbean rhythms and culture. Grace has also edited anthologies of poetry and was poet in residence at the Tate Gallery from 1999 to 2000.

Praise Song for My Mother is on page 45.

Sheena Patel (born 1987)

Sheena lives and works in London. She is part of collective 4 Brown Girls Who Write.
Let Me Count the Ways is on page 26.

Pascale Petit (born 1953)

Pascale was born in Paris, grew up in France and Wales and lives in Cornwall. She is of French/Welsh/Indian heritage. She began her artistic career as a sculptor, exhibiting work at venues including the Natural History Museum and on London Underground. Pascale's poetry has won a multitude of awards, including the 2018 RSL Ondaatje Prize for *Mama Amazonica* (2017) and the 2013 Manchester Poetry Prize for *Fauverie* (2014). She is a recipient of the inaugural RSL Literature Matters award and in 2018 became an RSL Fellow. Her works have been translated into eighteen languages. Pascale has taught at Tate Modern and Arvon, among others, and was a co-founding tutor of The Poetry School. She performs internationally.
Sky Ladder is on page 143.

Rachel Piercey

Rachel studied English Literature at Oxford, where she was President of the Oxford University Poetry Society and won the Newdigate Prize in 2008. She took her MA in Creative Writing at Royal Holloway in 2011. She has worked at the Poetry Society and for The Emma Press, where she co-edited pamphlets and anthologies. She tutors for The Poetry School and regularly visits schools, libraries and festivals encouraging children to read and write poetry. Rachel has published three collections of verse.
The worlds is on page 43.

Sylvia Plath (1932–1963)

Sylvia was fiercely ambitious and worked tirelessly on her poetry. She attempted suicide in 1953 and her experiences recovering in a clinic inspired her only novel, *The Bell Jar*. In 1956 she met poet Ted Hughes while studying at Cambridge University. They married and had two children, but she struggled to find time to write with young children to care for and a house to run, and her career stalled while his took off. The relationship broke down and a distraught Sylvia plunged into a creative frenzy, getting up at dawn to write the furious poems for which she is best remembered. She took her own life during the freezing February of 1963. Her first poetry book had appeared in 1960, and *Ariel*, the collection that cemented her extraordinary reputation, appeared two years after her death.

Southern Sunrise is on page 207.

Jessie Pope (1868–1941)

Jessie contributed articles, comic stories and poetry to newspapers and magazines including *Vanity Fair* and *Punch*. Her work often presented portraits of independent, resilient women. Her reputation plummeted because during the First World War, she published poetry – often not very good poetry – in the *Daily Mail* designed to drive readers to enlist, and encouraging the shaming of those who didn't.

War Girls is on page 126.

Sheenagh Pugh (born 1950)

Sheenagh has published nine collections of poetry and translations, two novels and a critical study of fan fiction. She also translates poems, mostly from German and sometimes from French and Ancient Greek, and taught creative writing at the University of Glamorgan. Sheenagh's interests include language, history, northern landscapes, snooker and cyberspace. She says she has been accused of being 'populist' and 'too accessible', and that she hopes both things are true.

What if this road is on page 50.

Shazea Quraishi

Shazea was born in Pakistan, grew up in Canada and lived in Madrid before moving to London where she works as a writer, teacher and translator. Her poems have been published in anthologies and magazines in the UK and the US. Her latest collection is *The Art of Scratching* (2015) and she is adapting her chapbook *The Courtesan's Reply* (2012) as a play.

You May Have Heard of Me is on page 46.

Lola Ridge (1873–1941)

Lola moved from Dublin to New York with her mother. Having married and separated from a goldmine owner, she worked as a copywriter, artists' model, factory worker, illustrator and educator, as well as writing poetry inspired by life on the Lower East Side. She and her second husband were socialist activists, taking part in protest marches and holding lively parties in their shabby apartment for other writers. Lola wrote about subjects considered shocking at the time, including race riots, but her book *The Ghetto and Other Poems* made an immediate impact. She was always sickly though this impression was reinforced by the fact that she lied about her age, so people – including the writer of her *New York Times* obituary – thought she was ten years younger than she actually was when she died.

The Destroyer is on page 94.

Michèle Roberts (born 1949)

Michèle is half French and divides her time between England and

France. She has worked as a librarian, secretary, teacher, journalist and hospital cleaner, often writing at night, but was able to write full-time when one of her novels, *Daughters of the House*, was shortlisted for the 1992 Booker Prize. She is currently Emeritus Professor of Creative Writing at the University of East Anglia. Michèle is a Fellow of the Royal Society of Literature and was created a Chevalier de l'Ordre des Arts et des Lettres by the French government, but declined an OBE because she is a republican. She has presented on BBC radio, judged several literary prizes and chaired the British Council's Literature Advisory Committee.

Flying to Italy is on page 95.

Rachel Rooney (born 1962)

Rachel worked for many years as a teacher of children with special needs, and now travels the country, performing at schools and festivals. She has written rhyming picture books and poetry collections including *My Life as a Goldfish* (2014), *A Kid in My Class* (2018) and *The Language of Cat* (2011), which was longlisted for the Carnegie Medal and won the 2012 CLiPPA award.

Target is on page 141.

Christina Rossetti (1830–1894)

In contrast to her brother, the wild-living Pre-Raphaelite artist and poet Dante Gabriel Rossetti, Christina was so devout that she abstained from playing chess or visiting the opera on religious grounds. She remained unmarried, and devoted herself to charity work, her family and poetry. Although she modelled for her brother and other artists, it tended to be for sacred subjects and she heartily disapproved of some of the Pre-Raphaelites' other muses, including the ill-starred Lizzie Siddal, her brother's obsession and – eventually – his wife. One of her best-loved poems is 'Goblin Market', in which one naughty sister is tempted by sticky enchanted treats.

De Profundis is on page 142.

Muriel Rukeyser (1913–1980)

Muriel was a lifelong political activist as well as an important figure in twentieth-century feminist literature, writing on subjects including equality, justice and Judaism. She reported from Barcelona during the Spanish Civil War, was jailed for protesting against the Vietnam War and travelled to Korea to demonstrate against poet Kim Chi-ha being sentenced to death (his execution did not go ahead). As well as writing and translating poetry, Muriel produced journalism, biography, plays, children's books and television scripts.

Darkness Music is on page 135.

Olive Runner

Olive's poem was published in *Poetry* magazine in September 1918. Almost a hundred years later, it was rediscovered and celebrated as part of the freedom-themed National Poetry Day 2017.

Freedom is on page 18.

Sappho (c. 630–c. 570 BC)

Not many facts are known about Sappho's life, but she lived on the Greek island of Lesbos – probably in Mytilene, the island's biggest city – and is thought to have had several brothers, a husband and a daughter. Most of her poems survive only as fragments, some of which were discovered in ancient Egyptian papier-mâché coffins in 1914. We do know that she was praised throughout the ancient world – Plato called her 'the tenth Muse' – and that her image appeared on statues and coins. At a time when most poetry was formal and meant for public

performance, Sappho wrote passionately about her private feelings, including love poems addressed to women. It is from her home island of Lesbos that we get the word 'lesbian'.
'Leave Krete' is on page 211.

Carole Satyamurti (1939–2019)

Carole, who worked as a social worker, then a Lecturer in Sociology at the University of East London, came to poetry relatively late in life. In her forties, she took a writing course and was astonished to win the National Poetry Competition. She went on to publish six collections of poetry, winning awards and Poetry Book Society recommendations. Carole also produced a retelling of the *Mahabharata*, an Indian epic poem.
Ourstory is on page 28.

Anna Seward (1742–1809)

Anna lived most of her life in the Bishop's Palace of Lichfield Cathedral, where her father, Thomas Seward, had served as Canon. Thomas had written in favour of female education, and he ensured Anna was taught to a high standard at home – she could, apparently, recite poems by Milton at the tender age of three. Anna went on to become one of the most prominent writers of her day, publishing successful poetry collections and writing for periodicals, often engaging in furious disputes with other writers including James Boswell. She was critical of the institution of marriage and remained single, though she formed passionate attachments to women including her foster sister, Honora Sneyd, to whom she addressed several poems.
Extract from *Elegy on Captain Cook* is on page 163.

Anne Sexton (1928–1974)

Anne struggled with her mental health for most of her adult life and began writing poetry as a means of therapy. Many of the themes she tackled in her often rawly autobiographical poems were seen as shocking by critics at the time. She studied under Robert Lowell at Boston University alongside writers including Sylvia Plath, and her work was enormously successful. She won numerous honours and awards, including the Pulitzer Prize, and continues to be seen and studied as one of the greatest twentieth-century poets.

Her Kind is on page 121.

Izumi Shikibu (born c. 976)

Izumi was one of the greatest women poets of the Heian period, during which there was an extraordinary flowering of art and literature at the Japanese Imperial Court. She enjoyed numerous love affairs – including dalliances with two sons of the Emperor Reizei – and was married twice. Her scandalous love affairs made such an impression, they were immortalized in stories written in the following century. Her legacy includes over two hundred poems, many of them very sexy, including a poetic diary of her relationship with Prince Atsumichi.

'Out of the darkness' is on page 110.

Penelope Shuttle (born 1947)

Penelope has lived in Cornwall since 1970 and the county's mercurial weather and rich history are continuing sources of inspiration. So too is the personal and artistic union Penelope shared with her husband, the poet Peter Redgrove, until his untimely death in 2003. She has written five acclaimed novels as well as seven poetry collections, her *Selected Poems* (1998) being a Poetry Book Society Recommendation. She has been shortlisted for the T. S. Eliot Prize and the Forward

Poetry Prize, and has won an Eric Gregory Award.
Poem is on page 80.

May Sinclair (1863–1946)

May cut short her formal education to nurse her ill brothers, but educated herself through reading widely. She was one of Britain's leading female writers and critics, producing stories, novels, reviews, and biographies of the Brontës, as well as poetry, although her reputation had dwindled until her novels were revived in the 1980s. She is credited with coining the phrase 'stream of consciousness' to describe modernist writing. May was fascinated by psychoanalysis and worked at a psychiatric clinic from 1913. She also served, briefly, with an ambulance unit in Belgium during the First World War. A staunch feminist, May was active in the Suffragette movement. Though she had once circulated in the highest literary circles – counting Thomas Hardy, Ezra Pound, H.D. and Charlotte Mew among her acquaintances – she suffered in later life from Parkinson's disease and spent her last two decades in seclusion in Buckinghamshire.
The Chatelaine is on page 184.

Edith Sitwell (1887–1964)

Born into an upper-class Yorkshire family, Edith herself claimed that she was 'more alive than most people'. She was a forceful and outspoken personality, often decked out in enormous jewellery and dressed like her heroine Elizabeth I, and her poetry was original and mould-breaking. She also wrote history and criticism, and some of her poems, including the famous Second World War poem 'Still Falls the Rain', were set to music. Her poetry recitals were always dramatic occasions – some recordings of them survive – and she toured America in the 1940s.
The Lady with the Sewing-Machine is on page 122.

Maggie Smith (born 1977)

Maggie is the author of *Lamp of the Body* (2005), *The Well Speaks of Its Own Poison* (2015) and *Good Bones* (2017), as well as three prizewinning chapbooks. She has received fellowships from the National Endowment for the Arts, the Ohio Arts Council, and the Sustainable Arts Foundation, and works as a freelance writer and editor.

The Mother is on page 34.

Stevie Smith (1902–1971)

Christened Florence, Stevie got her nickname from the jockey Steve Donoghue because she was so small. She was mostly brought up by her beloved, fiercely independent aunt (whom she nicknamed 'Lion') and remained single, observing that marriage looked rather tiring. Stevie published poems illustrated with her own quirky doodles and rather autobiographical novels in which friends – including George Orwell, with whom she may have had an affair – thought they recognized themselves. She was fascinated by death and religion, and her lively readings won her fans, including Sylvia Plath, who called herself a 'desperate Smith-addict'. Though she often suffered from ill health and sadness, she had a mischievous sense of dark humour that shines through her poems.

My Hat / The Forlorn Sea are on pages 188 and 197.

Edith Södergran (1892–1923)

Edith was a Swedish-speaking Finnish poet born in St Petersburg during a turbulent time for Russia. Due to her father's poor health, her mother supported the family, giving Edith a strongly feminist role model. Edith fell ill herself and was sent to recover in a Swiss clinic where she met and was inspired by several writers. Her modern style of poetry was ahead of its time – critics were unimpressed, though her

About the Poets

work became hugely influential after her death from tuberculosis aged only thirty-one.

Strange Sea is on page 167.

Anne Spencer (1882–1975)

Anne was a poet, teacher, librarian and civil rights activist and, although she lived much of her life in Virginia, was a key member of the Harlem Renaissance, an explosion of African-American culture centred on New York. She was raised largely by her mother after her parents' separation and, although she didn't attend school until the age of eleven, she excelled in her education. Anne's poetry focused on themes of racial and sexual inequality as well as her deep love of nature – she was a keen gardener – and were widely anthologized. She and her husband Edward were active in the fight for civil rights and hosted figures including Martin Luther King and Langston Hughes at their home in Lynchburg, now a museum.

Translation is on page 215.

Ellie Steel

Ellie Steel is studying for her A Levels at Oxford Spires Academy.

Wings is on page 89.

Den Sute-Jo (1633–1698)

Den Sute-Jo came from a wealthy samurai family and was born in a small mountain town in northwestern Kyoto. She married her stepbrother and had five sons and one daughter. Both she and her husband studied poetry with the famous poet-scholar Kitamura Kigin. After she was widowed, she became a nun and then a Zen Buddhist, living in a temple close to her Zen master with other women.

'On the road through the clouds' is on page 137.

May Swenson (1913–1989)

May's parents were Swedish immigrants to Utah and English was her second language. Although they struggled to accept that she was lesbian, she remained close to her Mormon family all her life. May moved to New York in the 1930s and worked in academia and publishing before focusing on her own writing. She published collections of poetry for both adults and children during her lifetime, and several more were published posthumously. Her work won numerous awards, and she was a Chancellor of the Academy of American Poets from 1980 to 1989. *The Centaur* is on page 181.

Sara Teasdale (1884–1933)

Sara's poetry was hugely successful, and she won the first Pulitzer Prize in 1918 (when it was called the Columbia Poetry Prize). She had many suitors, including a poet, Vachel Lindsay, who felt he couldn't support her financially, so she married and later divorced another man instead. Afterwards, she rekindled her friendship with Lindsay, who was by now married with children. Two years after his death, Sara sadly took her own life.

On the South Downs is on page 106.

Kate Tempest (born 1985)

Kate was born in London in 1985. Her work includes the plays *Wasted*, *Glasshouse* and *Hopelessly Devoted*; the poetry collections *Hold Your Own* and *Running Upon the Wires*; the albums *Everybody Down*, *Balance* and *Let Them Eat Chaos*; the long poems *Brand New Ancients* and *Let Them Eat Chaos;* and her debut novel, *The Bricks that Built the Houses*. She was nominated for the Mercury Music prize for her debut album, *Everybody Down*, and received the Ted Hughes Award and a Herald Angel Award for *Brand New Ancients*. Kate was

also named a Next Generation poet in 2014.
The cypher is on page 85.

Sophia Thakur (born 1996)

Sophia is one of the most recognizable figures in UK performance poetry today, with a large following on YouTube and social media. She has collaborated with the likes of MTV, NIKE, TEDx and BET, and performed at some of the UK's biggest music festivals and venues, including Glastonbury and Tate Britain. Her first poetry collection, *Somebody Give This Heart a Pen*, was published in October 2019. *When to Write* is on page 83.

Michelle Tiwo

Michelle is an actor, poet, spoken word educator and founder of Sistren podcast. Their work featured in Barbican Young Poets 2016, and they have been commissioned by organizations including the Royal College of Art and The Floating Showroom. Michelle's work is reflective of their identity and their communities: Nigeria and Togo via South East London. Recent acting credits include *Parakeet, Ackee and Saltfish* on BBC3, *And The Rest of Me Floats* at the Bush Theatre and *The Ting* for Channel 4 Random Acts.
Maybe I'll Be The First is on page 3.

Katharine Towers (born 1961)

Katharine has published two poetry collections. *The Floating Man* won the Seamus Heaney Centre Prize, and *The Remedies* was shortlisted for the T. S. Eliot Prize. Katharine's poems have been widely published and read on BBC Radio 3 and 4, and one of the poems from *The Floating Man* was selected as a Poem on the Underground in London. Katharine teaches poetry workshops for the

Poetry Society and at universities and literary festivals.
Books is on page 75.

Vivien Urban

Vivien was born in Hungary but at the age of eleven moved to the UK, where she attended the Oxford Spires Academy and enjoyed writing poetry as a way to improve her English. Her poem 'Hungary' was included in the anthology *England: Poems from a School*, edited by Kate Clanchy, who taught her creative writing. Vivien studies English, Languages and Creative Writing at St Andrews University.
Hungary is on page 100.

Kate Wakeling

Kate is a musicologist and writer, whose debut collection of verse for children, *Moon Juice*, won the 2017 CLiPPA and was nominated for the 2018 Carnegie Medal. Her poetry for adults has been published in publications including the *Guardian, The Forward Book of Poetry 2016* and *The Best British Poetry 2014*. Kate is writer-in-residence with Aurora Orchestra and co-creator of Far Far Away, a series of children's storytelling concerts. She has performed at Shakespeare's Globe, the Cheltenham Literature Festival, the Southbank Centre and Wigmore Hall, among other venues. Kate also writes for publications including the *Times Literary Supplement* and *BBC Music Magazine*.
The Instructions is on page 12.

Phillis Wheatley (c. 1753–1784)

Phillis was seized from West Africa and sold into slavery in the household of John Wheatley in Boston aged only seven. The Wheatleys did not excuse her from domestic work but they did ensure that she was well educated, and she began to write and publish poetry in her teens. Phillis always enjoyed greater success in England than in America, and she visited London and met dignitaries including Benjamin Franklin in 1771. After the Wheatleys died, Phillis married a free black man called John Peters, but in the harsh job market following the American Civil War they descended into poverty. She died, along with their last surviving child, while John was languishing in a debtors' prison, though she never stopped writing and endeavouring to publish her work.

Extract from *On Imagination* is on page 180.

Anna Wickham (1883–1947)

Born Edith Alice Mary Harper, Anna moved between Australia, France and the UK – her pseudonymous surname was inspired by a Brisbane street. Her possessive husband tried to put an end to her singing and writing career, and she suffered a breakdown and a brief spell in an asylum. Anna published several collections of poetry which were hugely popular especially in America, and had many literary friends, including Katherine Mansfield and H.D. Those friendships, however, were sometimes tempestuous: she was rumoured to have once thrown poet Dylan Thomas out of her house during a snowstorm.

Divorce is on page 52.

Ella May Wiggins (1900–1929)

Ella was active in the National Textile Workers Union, fighting for workers' rights in Gastonia, North Carolina, where she worked as a spinner. Four of her nine children died of whooping cough after the mill superintendent refused to change her from the night to the day shift to tend them. When she quit her job to look after them, she couldn't afford the medicine to save them. Ella wrote and sang her ballads to support the cause. In 1929, at the height of the workers' strikes, she was shot and killed by five Loray Mill employees, who were exonerated despite over fifty witnesses to the murder.

All Around the Jailhouse is on page 114.

Ella Wheeler Wilcox (1850–1919)

Born to Wisconsin farmers, Ella wrote to support her family. Her mildly steamy poems were hugely popular with readers, though critics snobbishly included her poems in some anthologies of 'worst poems'. During the First World War, Ella believed that her husband instructed her from beyond the grave to visit the Allied Forces in France to boost morale which she duly did, reciting poems to the troops.

The Winds of Fate is on page 170.

Chrissy Williams

Chrissy grew up in Devon and now lives in London. Her first collection, *Bear*, was named as one of the *Daily Telegraph*'s Fifty Best Books of 2017. She founded the Free Verse: Poetry Book Fair and co-edits the world first edible poetry magazine, *Poetry Digest*, which prints poetry on cakes. She has read at venues including the Royal Albert Hall and the Southbank Centre, and on BBC Radio 3. Chrissy is bilingual Italian and also works as a tutor and an editor, including for comics and videogame magazines.

Devil at the End of Love is on page 146.

Elinor Wylie (1885–1928)

Elinor published four collections of poetry and four novels in the last four years of her life, as well contributing to magazines including *Vanity Fair*. Her work won praise from writers including Edna St Vincent Millay, and her first novel was famously launched with a torchlit procession through the streets of Manhattan. She lived a rather tempestuous personal life and was married three times. Elinor's work was much admired during her lifetime and, though her reputation diminished in the mid-twentieth century, her position as an important modernist writer is now recognized.

Escape is on page 9.

Sun Yün-feng (1764–1814)

Sun Yün-feng was the daughter of an official and married a scholar. She was a favourite student of the Ch'ing dynasty poet Yüan Mei, who is notable for supporting women's poetry during an era when it was suppressed.

On the Road Through Chang-te is on page 51.

Belinda Zhawi

Belinda was born in Zimbabwe and moved to London aged twelve. She studied at Westminster and Goldsmiths and went on to be a 2015/16 London Laureate and the 2016/17 Institute of Contemporary Arts Associate Poet. She co-founded community and performance platform BORN::FREE, and has been the Serpentine Gallery Schools Artist-in-Residence. Belinda published the poetry pamphlet *Small Inheritances* in 2018 and also works in London's jazz and beatmaking scene.

Dzoka (Return) is on page 212.

Index of First Lines

Index of Poets

Acknowledgements

An enormous and heartfelt thank you to every poet who has given permission for us to include their work in this book. I'm extremely star-struck around poets, because they are magic. Thank you all for writing such extraordinarily brilliant work and sharing it with us. I'm also immensely grateful for all the women from centuries past for writing and publishing despite everything that was stacked them. I hope you'll find new homes in the hearts of new readers who pick up this book.

Thanks always to wonderful Gaby Morgan: you are a brilliant publisher and I feel extremely lucky to have you as my editor. Huge thanks also to design genius Rachel Vale, Publicity and Marketing dream team Amber Ivatt and Maria Higgins, to Simran Sandhu and Charlie Selvaggi-Castelletti for their tenacity in tracking down even the most obscure of permissions and to the whole Macmillan Children's team for all their hard work getting this book into readers' hands.

Special thanks to the fast fingers of Charlie Selvaggi-Castelletti, Rachel Petty, Arub Ahmed and Cate Augustin for typing up the manuscript during lockdown. Thanks, finally, to my daughters, Sophie and Laura, for occupying themselves with a minimum of howling and fighting as I completed this book during lockdown and my husband Mark, for being so supportive despite his firm belief that the rude limerick is the only true poetic form.

The compiler and publisher would like to thank the following for permission to use their copyright material:

Adcock, Fleur: 'London' from *Poems 1960-2000* (Bloodaxe, 2000). Copyright © Fleur Adcock. Used with kind permission of the publisher. **Allnut, Gillian:** 'Ode' from *How the Bicycle Shone: New & Selected Poems* (Bloodaxe Books, 2007). Copyright © Gillian Allnut. Used with kind permission of the publisher. **Awolola, Ruth:** 'Wolves' by Ruth Awolola. Copyright © Ruth Awolola. Used by kind permission of the author. **Beer, Patricia:** 'Birthday Poem from Venice' from *Collected Poems* (Carcanet Press, 1990). Copyright © Patricia Beer. Used with permission of the publisher. **Bellamacina, Greta:** 'New Glass' from *Tomorrow's Woman* (Andrews McMeel Publishing, 2020). Copyright © Greta Bellamacina. Used with permission of the agent. **Benson, Fiona:** Wood Song' from *Vertigo & Ghost* (Vintage, 2019). Copyright © Fiona Benson. Used with permission of the publisher. **Berry, Liz:** 'The Burning' by Liz Berry. Copyright © Liz Berry. Used with kind permission of the author. **Bird, Caroline:** 'Megan married Herself' from *In These Days of Prohibition* (Carcanet Press, 2017). Copyright © Caroline Bird. Used with kind permission of Carcanet Press Limited, Manchester, UK. **Boland, Eavan:** 'The Pomegranate' from *Collected Poems* (Carcanet Press, 1995). Copyright © Eavan Boland. Used with kind permission of Carcanet Press Limited, Manchester, UK. **Bryce, Colette:** 'The Full Indian Rope Trick' from *The Full Indian Rope Trick* (Picador, 2004). Copyright © Colette Bryce. Used with permission of the publisher. **Burke, Helen:** 'The Road Out of Town' from *Today the Birds Will Sing: collected poems 1969-2016* (Valley Press, 2017). Copyright © Helen Burke. Used with permission of the publisher. **Cadbury, Helen:** 'Functional Skills Maths' from *Forever, Now* (Valley Press, 2017). Copyright © Helen Cadbury. Used with permission of the publisher. **Campbell, Jen:** 'December' by Jen Campbell. Copyright © Jen Campbell. Used with kind permission of the author. **Cannon, Moya:** 'Hunter's Moon' from *The Parchment Boat* (The Gallery Press, 1997). Copyright © Moya Cannon. Used by kind permission of the author and The Gallery press, Loughcrew, Oldcastle, Country Meath, Ireland. 'Driving Back Over the Blue Ridge' from *Hands* (Carcanet Press, 2012). Copyright © Moya Cannon. Used with kind permission of Carcanet Press Limited, Manchester, UK. **Carpenter, J R:** '*extract from* Notes on the Voyage of Owl and Girl' from *An Ocean of Static* (Penned in the Margins, 2018). Copyright © J R Carpenter. Used with kind permission of the publisher. **Chan, Mary Jean:** 'The Window',